HARRY POTTER
POTTER
AND THE
CURSED CHILD

—

PARTS ONE AND TWO
PLAYSCRIPT

BASED ON AN ORIGINAL NEW STORY BY

J.K. ROWLING
JOHN TIFFANY & JACK THORNE
A PLAY BY **JACK THORNE**

FIRST PRODUCED BY
SONIA FRIEDMAN PRODUCTIONS, COLIN CALLENDER
& HARRY POTTER THEATRICAL PRODUCTIONS

THE OFFICIAL SCRIPT OF THE
ORIGINAL WEST END PRODUCTION

THE DEFINITIVE AND FINAL PLAYSCRIPT

HARRY POTTER

AND THE
CURSED CHILD

—

**PARTS ONE AND TWO
PLAYSCRIPT**

sphere

SPHERE

First published in print in Great Britain in 2016 by Little, Brown
This paperback edition published in 2017 by Sphere

13

Text © Harry Potter Theatrical Productions Limited 2016
Potter family tree and Timeline © 2017 Pottermore Ltd

Harry Potter Publishing and Theatrical rights © J.K. Rowling

Artwork and logo are trademarks of and © Harry Potter Theatrical Productions Limited

Harry Potter characters, names and related indicia are trademarks of
and © Warner Bros. Ent. All rights reserved.

J.K. ROWLING'S WIZARDING WORLD is a trademark of J.K. Rowling
and Warner Bros. Entertainment Inc.

*All characters and events in this publication, other than those
clearly in the public domain, are fictitious and any resemblance
to real persons, living or dead, is purely coincidental.*

All rights reserved.
No part of this publication may be reproduced, stored in a
retrieval system, or transmitted, in any form, or by any means, without
the prior permission in writing of the publisher, nor be otherwise circulated
in any form of binding or cover other than that in which it is published
and without a similar condition including this condition being
imposed on the subsequent purchaser.

A CIP catalogue record for this book is available from the British Library.

ISBN 978-0-7515-6536-2

Typeset in Goudy by M Rules

Printed and bound in Great Britain by Clays Ltd, Elcograf S.p.A.

Papers used by Sphere are from well-managed forests
and other responsible sources.

Sphere
An imprint of
Little, Brown Book Group
Carmelite House
50 Victoria Embankment
London EC4Y 0DZ

An Hachette UK Company
www.hachette.co.uk

www.littlebrown.co.uk

CONTENTS

Harry Potter and the Cursed Child Parts One and Two
may not be performed in whole or in part and no use may
be made of it whatsoever except under express licence
from the rights holders of the work, J.K. Rowling and
Harry Potter Theatrical Productions Limited.
Please email enquiries@hptheatricalproductions.com
with any enquiries.

J.K. ROWLING

To Jack Thorne
who entered my world
and did beautiful things there.

JOHN TIFFANY

For Joe, Louis, Max, Sonny and Merle . . . wizards all . . .

JACK THORNE

To Elliott Thorne, born 7 April 2016.
As we rehearsed, he gurgled.

A CONVERSATION ABOUT READING SCRIPTS

*between director John Tiffany
and
playwright Jack Thorne*

Jack

The first play I ever read was *Joseph and the Amazing Technicolor Dreamcoat*. I was at primary school and very excited. I can't remember clearly, but think I mainly went through it looking for my lines. Yes, I was an obnoxious little brat and yes, I was going to play Joseph. The next play I read was *The Silver Sword*, a theatre adaptation of the Ian Serraillier classic. I wasn't going to play the lead in that – I think I played 'third boy' or something. I wanted to play Edek Balicki. I would have given anything to play Edek, but sadly my acting career was in terminal decline by then. I was nine years old.

John

The first script I ever read was *Oliver!* aged nine (even at that young age I was vaguely aware that the exclamation mark meant it was a musical – it's Oliver ... with songs!). I had been cast as the eponymous orphan in the Huddersfield Amateur Operatic Society's 1981 production. I have no memory of attempting to change my accent, so our production must have been a strange reimagining of Dickens's original in which Oliver's mother finds her way to a workhouse in West Yorkshire to give birth. Like you, I read through the script looking for my lines. I remember making a special trip to buy a fluorescent yellow pen so I could highlight Oliver's lines in my script, just like I'd noticed my fellow cast members do. Obviously, I thought, this was what marked you out as a seasoned performer. It was only later that the Artful Dodger pointed out that I not only had to highlight my lines, but also commit them to memory. And so began my lessons in reading plays.

Jack

I wish I'd seen your Oliver. And your highlighted script. I always admired your pristine brown directing notebooks. My scripts are – and always have been – dog-eared, covered in indecipherable notes and smeared with baby puke (okay, the puke is a relatively new addition).

So how do you think scripts should be read? How can they be read? When I was trying to write the stage directions for publication – in those final few weeks of scramble before we opened – I got really worried about all this. I remember in rehearsals we'd delete chunks of the script because the actors were communicating something effortlessly with a look so they didn't need the lines I'd written. This script was created for a particular group of actors, but others need to inhabit the roles too. The reader needs to visualise the characters, as does the director.

When you're reading a script for the first time, what are you looking for?

John

As a director, the first time you read a new script is very precious. It's the closest you're ever going to be to an audience watching a production of this script for the first time. Reading a finished script should allow us access to the story, its characters and the themes the playwright is exploring. A script can make us laugh and cry. It can take us through the joy of its story and also make us feel deep despair for the suffering of its characters. A script builds towards a fully realised production and an experience that can be shared with the audience.

As a playwright, how much of this full experience do you imagine when you are writing a script? Do you speak the characters' lines out loud as you type them?

Jack

I do worse than that, I move like them. Which, when you're working in well-known coffee shops and sandwich retailers, can lead to you attracting some strange looks. I find myself twisting into the character and gesticulating like them. It's all very embarrassing.

The thing that was perhaps most interesting about the process of writing this particular script is that I have never spent more time with actors – ever. Through the weeks of workshops and then weeks of rehearsals we were all in those rooms together for so long, all of us, from the design team to the sound team to the lights. I don't think any of us have experienced anything like that – I think it probably works out at eight months or so, all in all. What effect would you say that had on what was created? I'm sure it made it all a lot better, but more than that do you think it somehow changed the tone of what we did?

John

I love the thought of you sitting in cafés mumbling and contorting yourself into characters from your plays! I think there's probably an audience for this, Jack. It sounds like a very unique style of performance. We could tour it. I know the actors from *Cursed Child* and I would book front row seats. No? Well, okay then . . .

I definitely think that the significant amount of time we all spent together in workshops and rehearsals had a positive effect on what we created. The whole process still seems so vivid, dynamic and clear. From the initial story meetings we had with Jo at the beginning of 2014 through to the audiences who first saw the production in summer 2016, there have been so many actors, creatives, artists, producers, production and technical teams who have contributed to this play. This is the main reason I was so keen to include all their names in the published script. It's also why the published script can only ever be a gateway to the full experience of watching the production in a theatre.

So, as the writer of this script, what do you hope happens inside the imaginations of people reading the play who haven't, as yet, been able to see the production?

Jack

I think that's a difficult question to answer. On the day before the play opened, I wrote a tweet which said 'I'd love people to see it, it's better seen than read – plays are like sheet music, meant to be sung & we've a cast & crew of pure Beyoncé'. So maybe that's the answer: that they imagine the Beyoncés of the acting world – emotional and empathetic titans – killing every line with their subtlety and grace (because that's the reality, our cast are extraordinary) – and staging and movement and costume and lighting and video and sound that are all just sublime.

Or maybe I just hope they're able to read it as I wrote it – with Jo on one shoulder and you, John, on the other – trying my best to express in every single line the emotional truth and honesty that runs through the Harry Potter books. The difficult thing of course is the subtext between the lines, the way that looks can carry emotion, and the impossibility of truly capturing internal monologue in a script. In prose you can write how someone feels, and in the production the cast reflect the internal monologue on their faces. Plus, there's loads of magic stuff onstage, which I can't explain because it'll ruin watching the show and get Jamie

Harrison (Illusions and Magic) thrown out of the Magic Circle!
Maybe they can act it themselves in their head? Maybe they can
be as mad as me and sit in a café and play all the parts? How
would you say people should read it?

John

As you say, in prose you can express the truth of how someone
feels through internal monologue and give visual detail through
rich description, whereas we have our actors and creative collab-
orators who work with us to bring these elements to life on stage.
Even then, we often rely on the audiences' collective imagination
to make a particular moment of storytelling come to full-blooded
fruition. It's one of the reasons that I am so passionate about
theatre; film has computer-generated imagery but we have the
imagination of the audience. Both are extremely powerful.

I think there's something wonderful about the idea of readers
acting out the script in their heads. Or with their mates in their
bedrooms. Maybe there's a connection between this and our live
audiences' imagination. We will work hard so that everyone who
wants to see our production of *Harry Potter and The Cursed Child*
is able to, whether at the Palace Theatre in London or in new
productions elsewhere. In the meantime, I'm genuinely excited
about the countless productions that are happening in our readers' imaginations as they absorb your play.

PART ONE

PART ONE
ACT ONE

ACT ONE SCENE ONE

KING'S CROSS

*A busy and crowded station, full of people trying to go somewhere.
Amongst the hustle and bustle, two large cages rattle on top of two
laden trolleys. They're being pushed by two boys, JAMES POTTER and
ALBUS POTTER. Their mother, GINNY, follows after. A thirty-seven-
year-old man, HARRY, has his daughter LILY on his shoulders.*

ALBUS
    Dad. He keeps saying it.

HARRY
    James, give it a rest.

JAMES
    I only said he might be in Slytherin. And he might, so . . .
    (off his dad's glare) fine.

ALBUS *(looking up at his mum)*
    You'll write to me, won't you?

GINNY
    Every day if you want us to.

ALBUS
    No. Not every day. James says most people only get letters
    from home about once a month. I don't want to . . .

HARRY
    We wrote to your brother three times a week last year.

ALBUS
What? James!

ALBUS looks accusingly at JAMES, who grins back.

GINNY
Yes. You may not want to believe everything he tells you
about Hogwarts. He likes a laugh, your brother.

JAMES
Can we go now please?

ALBUS looks at his dad, and then his mum.

GINNY
All you have to do is walk straight at the wall between
platforms nine and ten.

LILY
I'm so excited.

HARRY
Don't stop and don't be scared you'll crash into it, that's
very important. Best to do it at a run if you're nervous.

ALBUS
I'm ready.

*HARRY and LILY put their hands on ALBUS's trolley – GINNY
joins JAMES's trolley – and together, the family run hard
into the barrier.*

ACT ONE   SCENE TWO

PLATFORM NINE AND THREE-QUARTERS

Which is covered in thick white steam pouring from the HOGWARTS EXPRESS.

And which is also busy – but instead of people in sharp suits going about their day, it's now wizards and witches in robes mostly trying to work out how to say goodbye to their beloved progeny.

ALBUS
This is it.

LILY
Wow!

ALBUS
Platform nine and three-quarters.

LILY
Where are they? Are they here? Maybe they didn't come?

> HARRY *points out* RON, HERMIONE *and their daughter* ROSE. LILY *runs hard up to them.*

Uncle Ron. Uncle Ron!!!

> RON *turns towards them as* LILY *goes barrelling up to him. He picks her up into his arms.*

RON
If it isn't my favourite Potter.

LILY

Have you got my trick?

RON

Are you aware of the Weasleys' Wizard Wheezes certified nose-stealing breath?

ROSE

Mum! Dad's doing that lame thing again.

HERMIONE

You say lame, he says glorious, I say . . . somewhere in between.

RON

Hang on. Let me just munch this . . . air. And now it's just a simple matter of . . . excuse me if I smell slightly of garlic . . .

He breathes on her face. LILY *giggles.*

LILY

You smell of porridge.

RON

Bing. Bang. Boing. Young lady, get ready to not being able to smell at all . . .

He lifts her nose off.

LILY

Where's my nose?

RON

Tada!

His hand is empty. It's a lame trick. Everyone enjoys its lameness.

LILY

You are silly.

ALBUS

Everyone's staring at us again.

RON

Because of me! I'm extremely famous. My nose experiments are legendary!

HERMIONE
They're certainly something.

HARRY
Parked all right then?

RON
I did. Hermione didn't believe I could pass a Muggle driving test, did you? She thought I'd have to Confund the examiner.

HERMIONE
I thought nothing of the kind, I have complete faith in you.

ROSE
And I have complete faith he did Confund the examiner.

RON
Oi!

ALBUS
Dad . . .

ALBUS *pulls on* HARRY's *robes*. HARRY *looks down*.

Do you think – what if I am – what if I'm put in Slytherin . . .

HARRY
And what would be wrong with that?

ALBUS
Slytherin is the house of the snake, of Dark Magic . . . it's not a house of brave wizards.

HARRY
Albus Severus, you were named after two headmasters of Hogwarts. One of them was a Slytherin and he was probably the bravest man I ever knew.

ALBUS
But just say . . .

HARRY
If it matters to you, *you*, the Sorting Hat will take your feelings into account.

ALBUS
Really?

HARRY

It did for me.

This is something he's never said before, it resonates around his head a moment.

Hogwarts will be the making of you, Albus. I promise you, there is nothing to be frightened of there.

JAMES (*sharply*)

Apart from the Thestrals. Watch out for the Thestrals.

ALBUS

I thought they were invisible!

HARRY

Listen to your professors, *don't* listen to James, and remember to enjoy yourself. Now, if you don't want this train to leave without you, you should leap on . . .

LILY

I'm going to chase the train out.

GINNY

Lily, come straight back.

HERMIONE

Rose. Remember to send Neville our love.

ROSE

Mum, I can't send a professor love!

ROSE exits for the train. And then ALBUS turns and hugs GINNY and HARRY one last time before following after her.

ALBUS

Okay, then. Bye.

He climbs on board. HERMIONE, GINNY, RON and HARRY stand watching the train – as whistles blow up and down the platform.

GINNY

They're going to be okay, right?

HERMIONE

Hogwarts is a big place.

RON
> Big. Wonderful. Full of food. I'd give anything to be going back.

HARRY
> Strange, Al being worried he'll be sorted into Slytherin.

HERMIONE
> That's nothing, Rose is worried whether she'll break the Quidditch scoring record in her first or second year. And how early she can take her O.W.Ls.

RON
> I have no idea where she gets her ambition from.

GINNY
> And how would you feel Harry, if Al – if he is?

RON
> You know Gin, we always thought there was a chance you could be sorted into Slytherin.

GINNY
> What?

RON
> Honestly, Fred and George ran a book.

HERMIONE
> Can we go? People are looking, you know.

GINNY
> People always look when you three are together. And apart. People always look at you.

> *The four exit.* GINNY *stops* HARRY.

> Harry . . . he'll be all right, won't he?

HARRY
> Of course he will.

ACT ONE   SCENE THREE

THE HOGWARTS EXPRESS

ALBUS *and* ROSE *walk along the carriage of the train. One full of dread, the other full of excitement.*

The TROLLEY WITCH *approaches from the opposite direction, pushing her trolley.*

TROLLEY WITCH
Anything from the trolley, dears? Pumpkin Pasty? Chocolate Frog? Cauldron Cake?

ROSE (*spotting* ALBUS's *loving look at the Chocolate Frogs*)
Al. We need to concentrate.

ALBUS
Concentrate on what?

ROSE
On who we choose to be friends with. My mum and dad met your dad on their first Hogwarts Express you know . . .

ALBUS
So we need to choose now who to be friends with for life? That's quite scary.

ROSE
On the contrary, it's exciting. I'm a Granger-Weasley, you're a Potter – everyone will want to be friends with us, we've got the pick of anyone we want.

ALBUS

So how do we decide – which compartment to go in . . .

ROSE

We rate them all and then we make a decision.

> ALBUS *opens a compartment door – to look in on a lonely blond kid –* SCORPIUS *– in an otherwise empty compartment.* ALBUS *smiles.* SCORPIUS *smiles back.*

ALBUS

Hi. Is this compartment . . .

SCORPIUS

It's free. It's just me.

ALBUS

Great. So we might just – come in – for a bit – if that's okay?

SCORPIUS

That's okay. Hi.

ALBUS

Albus. Al. I'm – my name is Albus . . .

SCORPIUS

Hi Scorpius. I mean, *I'm* Scorpius. You're Albus. I'm Scorpius. And you must be . . .

> ROSE's *face is growing colder by the minute.*

ROSE

Rose.

SCORPIUS

Hi Rose. Would you like some of my Fizzing Whizzbees?

ROSE

I've just had breakfast, thanks.

SCORPIUS

I've also got some Shock-o-Choc, Pepper Imps and some Jelly Slugs. Mum's idea – she says (*sings*), 'Sweets they always help you make friends' (*he realises that singing was a mistake*). Stupid idea probably.

ALBUS

I'll have some ... Mum doesn't let me have sweets. Which one would you start with?

ROSE *hits* ALBUS, *out of sight of* SCORPIUS.

SCORPIUS

Easy. I've always regarded the Pepper Imp as the king of the confectionery bag. They're peppermint sweets that make you smoke at the ears.

ALBUS

Brilliant, then that's what I'll— (ROSE *hits him again*.) Rose, will you please stop hitting me?

ROSE

I'm not hitting you.

ALBUS

You are hitting me, and it hurts.

SCORPIUS's *face falls*.

SCORPIUS

She's hitting you because of me.

ALBUS

What?

SCORPIUS

Listen, I know who you are, so it's probably only fair you know who I am.

ALBUS

What do you mean you know who I am?

SCORPIUS

You're Albus Potter. She's Rose Granger-Weasley. And I am Scorpius Malfoy. My parents are Astoria and Draco Malfoy. Our parents – they didn't get on.

ROSE

That's putting it mildly. Your mum and dad are Death Eaters!

SCORPIUS (*affronted*)
    Dad was – but Mum wasn't.

    ROSE *looks away, and* SCORPIUS *knows why she does.*

    I know what the rumour is, and it's a lie.

    ALBUS *looks from an uncomfortable* ROSE *to a desperate*
    SCORPIUS.

ALBUS
    What – is the rumour?

SCORPIUS
    The *rumour* is that my parents couldn't have children. That
    my father and my grandfather were so desperate for a powerful
    heir, to prevent the end of the Malfoy line, that they . . . that
    they used a Time-Turner to send my mother back—

ALBUS
    To send her back where?

ROSE
    The rumour is that he's Voldemort's son, Albus.

    A horrible, uncomfortable silence.

    It's probably rubbish. I mean . . . look, you've got a nose.

    The tension is slightly broken, SCORPIUS *laughs,*
    pathetically grateful.

SCORPIUS
    And it's just like my father's! I got his nose, his hair and his
    name. Not that that's a great thing either. I mean – father-
    son issues, I have them. But, on the whole, I'd rather be a
    Malfoy than, you know, the son of the Dark Lord.

    SCORPIUS *and* ALBUS *look at each other and something*
    passes between them.

ROSE
    Yes, well, we probably should sit somewhere else. Come on,
    Albus.

ALBUS *is thinking deeply.*

ALBUS
No (*off* ROSE's *look*), I'm okay. You go on ...

ROSE
Albus. I won't wait.

ALBUS
And I wouldn't expect you to. But I'm staying here.

ROSE *looks at him a second and then leaves the compartment.*

ROSE
Fine!

SCORPIUS *and* ALBUS *are left – looking at each other – unsure.*

SCORPIUS
Thank you.

ALBUS
No. No. I didn't stay – for you – I stayed for your sweets.

SCORPIUS
She's quite fierce.

ALBUS
Yes. Sorry.

SCORPIUS
No. I like it. Do you prefer Albus or Al?

SCORPIUS *grins and pops two sweets in his mouth.*

ALBUS (*thinks*)
Albus.

SCORPIUS (*as smoke comes out of his ears*)
THANK YOU FOR STAYING FOR MY SWEETS, ALBUS!

ALBUS (*laughing*)
Wow.

ACT ONE   SCENE FOUR

TRANSITION SCENE

And now we enter a never-world of time change. And this scene is all about magic.

The changes are rapid as we leap between worlds. There are no individual scenes, but fragments, shards that show the constant progression of time.

Initially we're inside Hogwarts, in the Great Hall, and everyone is dancing around ALBUS.

POLLY CHAPMAN
Albus Potter.

KARL JENKINS
A Potter. In our year.

YANN FREDERICKS
He's got his hair. He's got hair just like him.

ROSE
And he's my cousin. (*As they turn.*) Rose Granger-Weasley. Nice to meet you.

> *The* SORTING HAT *walks through the students who spring into their houses.*
>
> *It becomes quickly apparent he's approaching* ROSE, *who is tense as she awaits her fate.*

17

SORTING HAT

> I've done this job for centuries
> On every student's head I've sat
> Of thoughts I take inventories
> For I'm the famous Sorting Hat.

> I've sorted high, I've sorted low,
> I've done the job through thick and thin
> So put me on and you will know
> Which house you should be in . . .
> Rose Granger-Weasley.

He puts his hat on ROSE's *head.*

GRYFFINDOR!

There's cheering from the Gryffindors as ROSE *joins them.*

ROSE

Thank Dumbledore.

SCORPIUS runs to take ROSE's *place under the* SORTING
HAT's *glare.*

SORTING HAT

Scorpius Malfoy.

He puts his hat on SCORPIUS's *head.*

SLYTHERIN!

SCORPIUS was expecting this, he nods and half smiles.
There's cheering from the Slytherins as he joins them.

POLLY CHAPMAN

Well, that makes sense.

ALBUS walks swiftly to the front of the stage.

SORTING HAT

Albus Potter.

He puts his hat on ALBUS's *head – and this time he seems to take longer – almost like he too is confused.*

SLYTHERIN!

There's a silence.

A perfect, profound silence.

One that sits low, twists a bit and has damage within it.

POLLY CHAPMAN
Slytherin?

CRAIG BOWKER JR
Whoah! A Potter? In Slytherin.

ALBUS looks out, unsure. SCORPIUS *smiles, delighted, as he shouts across to him.*

SCORPIUS
You can stand next to me!

ALBUS *(thoroughly discombobulated)*
Right. Yes.

YANN FREDERICKS
I suppose his hair isn't that similar.

ROSE
Albus? But this is wrong, Albus. This is not how it's supposed to be.

And suddenly a flying lesson is happening with MADAM HOOCH.

MADAM HOOCH
Well, what are you all waiting for? Everyone stand by a broomstick. Come on, hurry up.

The kids all hurry into position beside their brooms.

Stick out your hands out over your broom, and say, 'Up!'

EVERYONE
UP!

ROSE's *and* YANN's *brooms sail into their hands.*

ROSE *and* YANN
> Yes!

MADAM HOOCH
> Come on now, I've no time for shirkers. Say 'UP'. 'UP' like you mean it.

EVERYONE *(bar* ROSE *and* YANN*)*
> UP!

> *Brooms sail up, including* SCORPIUS's*. Only* ALBUS *is left with his broom on the floor.*

EVERYONE *(bar* ROSE, YANN *and* ALBUS*)*
> YES!

ALBUS
> Up. UP. UP.

> *His broom doesn't move. Not even a millimetre. He stares at it with disbelieving desperation. There's giggling from the rest of the class.*

POLLY CHAPMAN
> Oh Merlin's beard, how humiliating! He really isn't like his father at all is he?

KARL JENKINS
> Albus Potter, the Slytherin Squib.

MADAM HOOCH
> Okay. Children. Time to fly.

> *And suddenly* HARRY *appears from nowhere beside* ALBUS *as steam expands all over the stage. We're back on platform nine and three-quarters and time has ticked on mercilessly.* ALBUS *is now a year older (as is* HARRY*, but less noticeably).*

ALBUS
> I'm just asking you Dad if you'll – if you'll just stand a little away from me.

HARRY *(amused)*
> Second-years don't like to be seen with their dads is that it?

An OVER-ATTENTIVE WIZARD *begins to circle them.*

ALBUS
No. It's just – you're *you* and – and I'm me and—

HARRY
It's just people looking okay? People look. And they're looking at me, not you.

The OVER-ATTENTIVE WIZARD *proffers something for* HARRY *to sign – he signs it.*

ALBUS
At Harry Potter and his disappointing son.

HARRY
What does that mean?

ALBUS
At Harry Potter and his Slytherin son.

JAMES *rushes past them carrying his bag.*

JAMES
Slythering Slytherin, stop with your dithering, time to get on to the train.

HARRY
Unnecessary, James.

JAMES *(long gone)*
See you at Christmas, Dad.

HARRY *looks at* ALBUS, *concerned.*

HARRY
Al—

ALBUS
My name is Albus, not Al.

HARRY
Are the other kids being unkind? Is that it? Maybe if you tried making a few more friends – without Hermione and Ron I wouldn't have survived Hogwarts, I wouldn't have survived at all.

ALBUS
> But I don't need a Ron and Hermione – I've – I've got a
> friend, Scorpius, and I know you don't like him but he's all
> I need.

HARRY
> Look, as long as you're happy, that's all that matters to me.

ALBUS
> You didn't need to bring me to the station, Dad.

> *ALBUS picks up his case and makes hard away.*

HARRY
> But I *wanted* to be here . . .

> *But* ALBUS *is gone.* DRACO MALFOY, *his robes perfect, his
> blond ponytail precisely placed, emerges from within the
> crowds to be beside* HARRY.

DRACO
> I need a favour.

HARRY
> Draco.

DRACO
> These rumours – about my son's parentage – they don't
> seem to be going away. The other Hogwarts students
> tease Scorpius about it relentlessly – if the Ministry could
> release a statement reaffirming that all Time-Turners were
> destroyed in the Battle of the Department of Mysteries . . .

HARRY
> Draco, just let it blow over – they'll soon move on.

DRACO
> My son is suffering and – Astoria hasn't been well
> recently – so he needs all the support he can get.

HARRY
> If you answer the gossip, you feed the gossip. There've been
> rumours Voldemort had a child for years, Scorpius is not
> the first to be accused. The Ministry, for your sake as well as
> ours, needs to steer well clear.

DRACO *frowns, annoyed, as the stage clears and* ROSE *and* ALBUS *stand ready with their cases.*

ALBUS

As soon as the train leaves you don't have to talk to me.

ROSE

I know. We just need to keep the pretence up in front of the grown-ups.

SCORPIUS *runs on – with big hopes and an even bigger case.*

SCORPIUS *(hopeful)*

Hi Rose.

ROSE *(definitive)*

Bye Albus.

SCORPIUS *(still hopeful)*

She's melting.

And suddenly we're in the Great Hall and PROFESSOR MCGONAGALL *is standing at the front, with a big smile on her face.*

PROFESSOR MCGONAGALL

And I'm pleased to announce Gryffindor's newest member of the Quidditch team – our – (*she realises she can't be partial*) your superb new Chaser – Rose Granger-Weasley.

The Hall erupts into cheers. SCORPIUS *claps alongside them all.*

ALBUS

Are you clapping her too? We hate Quidditch and she's playing for another house.

SCORPIUS

She's your cousin, Albus.

ALBUS

Do you think she'd clap for me?

SCORPIUS

I think she's brilliant.

The students circle ALBUS *again as suddenly a Potions class begins.*

POLLY CHAPMAN
Albus Potter. An irrelevance. Even portraits turn the other way when he comes up the stairs.

ALBUS *hunches over a potion.*

ALBUS
And now we add – is it horn of Bicorn?

KARL JENKINS
Leave him and Voldemort's child to it, I say.

ALBUS
With just a little salamander blood . . .

The potion explodes loudly.

SCORPIUS
Okay. What's the counter-ingredient? What do we need to change?

ALBUS
Everything.

And with that, time moves ever onwards – ALBUS*'s eyes become darker, his face grows more sallow. He's still an attractive boy, but he's trying not to admit it.*

And suddenly he's back on platform nine and three-quarters with his dad – who is still trying to persuade his son (and himself) that everything is okay. Both have aged another year.

HARRY
Third year. Big year. Here is your permission form for Hogsmeade.

ALBUS
I hate Hogsmeade.

HARRY
How can you hate a place you haven't actually visited yet?

ALBUS

    Because I know it'll be full of Hogwarts students.

    ALBUS screws up the paper.

HARRY

    Just give it a go – come on – this is your chance to go nuts in Honeydukes without your mum knowing – no Albus, don't you dare.

ALBUS *(pointing his wand)*

    Incendio!

    The ball of paper bursts into flame, and ascends across the stage.

HARRY

    Of all the stupid things!

ALBUS

    The ironic thing is I didn't expect it to work. I'm terrible at that spell.

HARRY

    Al–Albus, I've been exchanging owls with Professor McGonagall – she says you're isolating yourself – you're uncooperative in lessons – you're surly – you're—

ALBUS

    So what would you like me to do? Magic myself popular? Conjure myself into a new house? Transfigure myself into a better student? Just cast a spell, Dad, and change me into what you want me to be, okay? It'll work better for both of us. Got to go. Train to catch. Friend to find.

    ALBUS runs to SCORPIUS, who is sitting on his case – numb to the world.

    (delighted) Scorpius . . .

    (concerned) Scorpius . . . are you okay?

    SCORPIUS says nothing. ALBUS tries to read his friend's eyes.

Your mum? It's got worse?

SCORPIUS

It's got the worst it can possibly get.

ALBUS sits down beside SCORPIUS.

ALBUS

I thought you'd send an owl . . .

SCORPIUS

I couldn't work out what to say.

ALBUS

And now I don't know what to say . . .

SCORPIUS

Say nothing.

ALBUS

Is there anything . . .

SCORPIUS

Come to the funeral.

ALBUS

Of course.

SCORPIUS

And be my good friend.

And suddenly the SORTING HAT *is centre stage and we're back in the Great Hall.*

SORTING HAT

Are you afraid of what you'll hear?
Afraid I'll speak the name you fear?
Not Slytherin! Not Gryffindor!
Not Hufflepuff! Not Ravenclaw!
Don't worry, child, I know my job,
You'll learn to laugh, if first you sob.
Lily Potter. GRYFFINDOR!

LILY

Yes!

ALBUS

Great.

SCORPIUS

Did you really think she'd come to us? Potters don't belong in Slytherin.

ALBUS

This one does.

As he tries to melt into the background, the other students laugh. He looks up at them all.

I didn't choose, you know that? I didn't choose to be his son.

ACT ONE   SCENE FIVE

MINISTRY OF MAGIC, HARRY'S OFFICE

HERMIONE *sits with piles of paper in front of her in* HARRY's *messy office. She is slowly sorting through it all, reading and trying to understand.* HARRY *enters in a rush. He is bleeding from a graze on his cheek.* HERMIONE *looks up beadily.*

HERMIONE
How did it go?

HARRY *(smiles)*
It was true.

HERMIONE
Theodore Nott?

HARRY
In custody.

HERMIONE
And the Time-Turner itself?

> HARRY *reveals the Time-Turner. It shines out alluringly.*
> HERMIONE *is amazed to see it.*

Is it genuine? Does it work? It's not just an Hour-Reversal Turner – it goes back further?

HARRY
We don't know anything yet. I wanted to try it out there and then but wiser heads prevailed.

HERMIONE
Well, now we have it.

HARRY
And you're sure you want to keep it?

HERMIONE
I don't think we've a choice. Look at it. It's entirely different to the Time-Turner I had.

HARRY (*dryly*)
Apparently wizardry has moved on since we were kids.

HERMIONE
You're bleeding.

> **HARRY** *checks his face in the mirror. He dabs at the wound with his robes.*

Don't worry, it'll go with the scar.

HARRY (*with a grin*)
What you doing in my office, Hermione?

HERMIONE
I was anxious to hear about Theodore Nott and – thought I'd check whether you'd kept your promise and were on top of your paperwork.

HARRY
Ah. Turns out I'm not.

HERMIONE
No. You're not. Harry, how can you get any work done in this chaos?

> **HARRY** *waves his wand and the papers and books transform into neat piles.* **HARRY** *smiles.*

HARRY
No longer chaotic.

HERMIONE
But still ignored. You know there's some interesting stuff in here ... there are mountain trolls riding graphorns through Hungary, there are giants with winged tattoos on their backs walking through the Greek Seas, and the werewolves have gone entirely underground—

HARRY

Great, let's get out there. I'll get the team together.

HERMIONE

Harry, I get it. Paperwork's boring . . .

HARRY

Not for you.

HERMIONE

I'm busy enough with my own. These are people and beasts
that fought alongside Voldemort in the great wizarding
wars. These are allies of darkness. This – combined
with what we have just unearthed at Theodore Nott's –
could mean something. But if the Head of Magical Law
Enforcement isn't reading his files—

HARRY

But I don't need to read it – I'm out there, hearing about it.
Theodore Nott – it was me who heard the rumours about
the Time-Turner and me who acted upon it. You really don't
need to tell me off.

HERMIONE *looks at* HARRY *– this is tricky.*

HERMIONE

Do you fancy a toffee? Don't tell Ron.

HARRY

You're changing the subject.

HERMIONE

I truly am. Toffee?

HARRY

Can't. We're off sugar at the moment.

Beat.

You know, you can get addicted to that stuff?

HERMIONE

What can I say? My parents were dentists, I was bound to
rebel at some point. Forty is leaving it a little late, but . . .
(*she smiles at her friend*) Look, you've just done a brilliant
thing. You're certainly not being told off – I just need you

to look at your paperwork every now and again, that's all.
Consider this a gentle – nudge – (HARRY *scowls*) from the
Minister for Magic.

   HARRY *hears the implication in her emphasis; he nods.*

How's Ginny? How's Albus?

HARRY
It seems I'm as good at fatherhood as I am at paperwork.
How's Rose? How's Hugo?

HERMIONE (*with a grin*)
You know, Ron says he thinks I see more of my secretary
Ethel (*she indicates off*) than him. Do you think there's a
point where we made a choice – parent of the year or –
Ministry official of the year? Go on. Go home to your
family Harry, the Hogwarts Express is about to depart for
another year – enjoy the time you've got left – and then
come back here with a fresh head and get these files
read.

HARRY
You really think this could all mean something?

HERMIONE (*with a smile*)
It could do. But if it does, we'll find a way to fight it, Harry.
We always have.

   *She smiles once more – pops a toffee in her mouth and
leaves the office.* HARRY *is left alone. He packs his bag.
He walks out of the office and down a corridor. The
weight of the world upon his shoulders.*
   He walks, tired, into a telephone box. He dials 62442.

TELEPHONE BOX
Farewell, Harry Potter.

   He ascends away from the Ministry of Magic.

ACT ONE   SCENE SIX

HARRY AND GINNY POTTER'S HOUSE

ALBUS *can't sleep. He is sitting at the top of the stairs. He hears voices below him. We hear* HARRY's *voice before he's revealed. An elderly man in a wheelchair is with him,* AMOS DIGGORY.

HARRY

Amos, I understand, I really do – but I'm only just home and—

AMOS

I've tried to make appointments at the Ministry. They say 'Ah, Mr Diggory, we have an appointment for you, let's see, in two months.' I wait. Very patiently.

HARRY

—and coming to my house in the middle of the night – when my kids are just getting ready for their new year at school – it's not right.

AMOS

Two months pass, I receive an owl, 'Mr Diggory, I'm awfully sorry, but Mr Potter has been called away on urgent business, we're going to have to shift things around a little, are you available for an appointment in, let's see, two months' time.' And then it repeats again, and again ... You're shutting me out.

HARRY
Of course I'm not. It's just, I'm afraid, as Head of the Department of Magical Law Enforcement I'm responsible—

AMOS
There's plenty you're responsible for.

HARRY
Sorry?

AMOS
My son, Cedric, you do remember Cedric, don't you?

HARRY (remembering Cedric hurts him)
Yes, I remember your son. His loss—

AMOS
Voldemort wanted you! Not my son! You told me yourself, the words he said were 'kill the spare'. The spare. My son, my beautiful son, was a spare.

HARRY
Mr Diggory, as you know, I sympathise with your efforts to memorialise Cedric but—

AMOS
A memorial? I am not interested in a memorial – not any more. I am an old man – an old, dying man – and I am here to ask you – beg you – to help me get him back.

HARRY *looks up, astonished.*

HARRY
Get him back? Amos, that's not possible.

AMOS
The Ministry has a Time-Turner does it not?

HARRY
The Time-Turners were all destroyed.

AMOS
The reason I'm here with such urgency is I've just heard rumour – strong rumour – that the Ministry seized an illegal Time-Turner from Theodore Nott and has kept it. For investigation. Let me use that Time-Turner. Let me have my son back.

There's a long, deadly pause. HARRY *is finding this extremely difficult. We watch as* ALBUS *moves closer, listening.*

HARRY
Amos, playing with time? You know we can't do that.

AMOS
How many people have died for the Boy Who Lived? I'm asking you to save one of them.

This hurts HARRY. *He thinks, his face hardens.*

HARRY
Whatever you've heard – the Theodore Nott story is a fiction, Amos. I'm sorry.

DELPHI
Hello.

ALBUS *jumps a mile as* DELPHI – *twenty-something, determined and quirky – is revealed looking through the stairs at him.*

Oh. Sorry. Didn't mean to startle. I used to be a big stair-listener myself. Sitting there. Waiting for someone to say something the tiniest bit interesting.

ALBUS
Who are you? Because this is sort of my house and . . .

DELPHI
I'm a thief of course. I'm about to steal everything you own. Give me your gold, your wand and your Chocolate Frogs! (*She looks fierce and then smiles.*) Either that or I'm Delphini Diggory. (*She ascends the stairs and sticks out a hand.*) Delphi. I look after him – Amos – well, I try. (*She indicates* AMOS.) And you are?

ALBUS (*rueful grin*)
Albus.

DELPHI
Of course! Albus Potter! So Harry is your dad? That's a bit wow isn't it?

ALBUS
   Not really.

DELPHI
   Ah. Have I just put my foot in it? It's what they used to say
   about me at school. Delphini Diggory – there isn't a hole
   she couldn't dig herself into.

ALBUS
   They do all sorts with my name too.

   Pause. She looks at him carefully.

AMOS
   Delphi.

   She makes to depart and then hesitates. She smiles at
   ALBUS.

DELPHI
   We don't choose who we're related to. Amos isn't just my
   patient, he's my uncle, it's part of the reason I took the job
   at Upper Flagley. But that's made it difficult. It's tough to
   live with people stuck in the past, isn't it?

AMOS
   Delphi!

ALBUS
   Upper Flagley?

DELPHI
   St Oswald's Home for Old Witches and Wizards. Come see
   us some time. If you like.

AMOS
   DELPHI!

   She smiles and then trips as she travels down the stairs.
   She enters the room with AMOS *and* HARRY *in it.* ALBUS
   watches her.

DELPHI
   Yes, Uncle?

PART ONE

AMOS

Meet the once-great Harry Potter, now a stone-cold Ministry man. I will leave you in peace, sir. If peace is the right word for it. Delphi, my chair . . .

DELPHI

Yes, Uncle.

> AMOS *is pushed out of the room.* HARRY *is left, looking forlorn.* ALBUS *watches on, thinking, carefully.*

ACT ONE SCENE SEVEN

HARRY AND GINNY POTTER'S HOUSE, ALBUS'S ROOM

ALBUS *is sitting on the bed as the world goes on outside his door. Still against the constant motion outside. We hear a roar from* JAMES *(from off).*

GINNY
James, please, ignore your hair, and tidy that damn room . . .

JAMES
How can I ignore it? It's pink! I'm going to have to use my Invisibility Cloak!

JAMES *appears at the door, he has pink hair.*

GINNY
That's *not* why your dad gave you that cloak!

LILY
Who's seen my Potions book?

GINNY
Lily Potter, don't think you're wearing those to school tomorrow . . .

LILY *appears at* ALBUS's *door. She's wearing fairy wings that flutter.*

LILY
I love them. They're fluttery.

She exits as HARRY *appears in* ALBUS's *doorway. He looks through.*

HARRY
Hi.

There's an awkward pause between them. GINNY *appears in the doorway. She sees what's happening and stays a moment.*

Just delivering a pre-Hogwarts gift – gifts – Ron's sent this . . .

ALBUS
Okay, a love potion. Okay.

HARRY
I think it's a joke about – I don't know what. Lily got farting gnomes, James got a comb that's made his hair turn a shade of pink. Ron – well, Ron's Ron you know?

HARRY *puts down* ALBUS's *love potion on his bed.*

I also – this is from me . . .

He reveals a small blanket. GINNY *looks at it – she sees* HARRY *is trying, and then she softly walks away.*

ALBUS
An old blanket?

HARRY
I thought a lot about what to give you this year. James – well, James has been going on about the Invisibility Cloak since time itself, and Lily – I knew she'd love wings – but you. You're fourteen years old now, Albus, and I wanted to give you something which – meant something. This – is the last thing I had from my mum. The only thing. I was given to the Dursleys wrapped in it. I thought it had gone forever and then – when your Great Aunt Petunia died, hidden amongst her possessions, surprisingly, Dudley found this – and he kindly sent it on to me, and ever since then – well,

38

any time I've wanted luck I've found it and just tried to hold it and I wondered if you . . .

ALBUS

Wanted to hold it too? Okay. Done. Let's hope it brings me luck. I certainly need some.

He touches the blanket.

But you should keep it.

HARRY

I think – believe – Petunia wanted me to have it, that's why she kept it and now I want you to have it from me. I didn't really know my mother – but I think she'd have wanted you to have it too. And maybe I could come find you – and it – on Hallows' Eve. I'd like to be with it on the night they died – and that could be good for the two of us . . .

ALBUS

Listen, I've got quite a lot of packing to do, and you undoubtedly have Ministry work coming out of your ears so . . .

HARRY

Albus, I want you to have the blanket.

ALBUS

And do what with it? Fairy wings make sense, Dad, Invisibility Cloaks, they also make sense – but this – really?

HARRY *is slightly heartbroken. He looks at his son, desperate to reach out.*

HARRY

Do you want a hand? Packing. I always loved packing. It meant I was leaving Privet Drive and going back to Hogwarts. Which was . . . well, I know you don't love it but . . .

ALBUS

For you, it's the greatest place on earth. I know. The poor orphan, bullied by his Uncle and Aunt Dursley—

HARRY
　　Albus, please – can we just—

ALBUS
　　—traumatised by his cousin Dudley, saved by Hogwarts. I
　　know it all, Dad. Blah blah blah.

HARRY
　　I'm not going to rise to your bait, Albus Potter.

ALBUS
　　The poor orphan who went on to save us all – so may I
　　say – on behalf of wizarding kind. How grateful we are for
　　your heroism. Should we bow now or will a curtsey do?

HARRY
　　Albus, please – you know, I've never wanted gratitude.

ALBUS
　　But right now I'm overflowing with it – it must be the kind
　　gift of this mouldy blanket that did it . . .

HARRY
　　Mouldy blanket?

ALBUS
　　What did you think would happen? We'd hug. I'd tell you I
　　always loved you. What? What?

HARRY (*finally losing his temper*)
　　You know what? I'm done with being made responsible
　　for your unhappiness. At least you've got a dad. Because I
　　didn't, okay?

ALBUS
　　And you think that was unlucky? I don't.

HARRY
　　You wish me dead?

ALBUS
　　No! I just wish you weren't my dad.

HARRY (*seeing red*)
　　Well, there are times I wish you weren't my son.

　　　There's a silence. ALBUS *nods. Pause.* HARRY *realises what*
　　　he's said.

No, I didn't mean that . . .

ALBUS
Yes. You did.

HARRY
Albus, you just know how to get under my skin . . .

ALBUS
You meant it, Dad. And, honestly, I don't blame you.

There's a horrible pause.

You should probably leave me alone now.

HARRY
Albus, please . . .

ALBUS *picks up the blanket and throws it. It collides with
Ron's love potion, which spills all over the blanket and the
bed, producing a small puff of smoke.*

ALBUS
No luck or love for me, then.

ALBUS *runs out of the room.* HARRY *goes after him.*

HARRY
Albus. Albus . . . please . . .

ACT ONE   SCENE EIGHT

DREAM, HUT-ON-THE-ROCK

There's a LARGE BOOM. Then there's a LARGE CRASH. DUDLEY
DURSLEY, AUNT PETUNIA *and* UNCLE VERNON *are cowering behind a
bed.*

DUDLEY DURSLEY
Mum, I don't like this.

AUNT PETUNIA
I knew we made a mistake coming here. Vernon. Vernon.
There's nowhere we can hide. Not even a lighthouse is far
enough away!

There's another LARGE BOOM.

UNCLE VERNON
Hold on. Hold on. Whatever it is, it's not coming in here.

AUNT PETUNIA
We're cursed! He's cursed us! The boy has cursed us! (*Seeing*
YOUNG HARRY.) This is all your fault. Get back in your hole.

YOUNG HARRY *flinches as* UNCLE VERNON *holds out his
rifle.*

UNCLE VERNON
Whoever's there I should warn you – I'm armed.

There's a MASSIVE SMASH. And the door falls off its hinges. HAGRID stands in the middle of the door. He looks at them all.

HAGRID

Couldn't make us a cup o' tea, could yeh? It's not been an easy journey.

DUDLEY DURSLEY

Look. At. Him.

UNCLE VERNON

Stand back. Stand back. Behind me, Petunia. Behind me, Dudley. I'll soon see this scarramanger off.

HAGRID

Scarrawhat? (*He picks up* UNCLE VERNON's *gun.*) Haven't seen one of these for a while. (*He twists the end of the gun and ties it in a knot.*) Oops-a-daisy. (*And then he gets distracted. He's seen* YOUNG HARRY.) Harry Potter.

YOUNG HARRY

Hello.

HAGRID

Las' time I saw yeh, yeh was only a baby. Yeh look a lot like yer dad, but yeh've got yer mum's eyes.

YOUNG HARRY

You knew my parents?

HAGRID

Where's me manners? A very happy birthday to yeh. Got summat fer yeh here – I mighta sat on it at some point, but it'll taste all right.

From inside his coat he pulls a slightly squashed chocolate cake with 'Happy Birthday Harry' written on it in green icing.

YOUNG HARRY

Who are you?

HAGRID (*laughing*)

True, I haven't introduced meself. Rubeus Hagrid, Keeper of

Keys and Grounds at Hogwarts. (*He looks around himself.*)
What about that tea then, eh? I'd not say no ter summat
stronger if yeh've got it, mind.

YOUNG HARRY
Hogwhere?

HAGRID
Hogwarts. Yeh'll know all about Hogwarts, o' course.

YOUNG HARRY
Er – no. Sorry.

HAGRID
Sorry? It's them as should be sorry! I knew yeh weren't
gettin' yer letters but I never thought yeh wouldn't even
know abou' Hogwarts, fer cryin' out loud! Did yeh never
wonder where yer parents learnt it all?

YOUNG HARRY
Learnt what?

HAGRID *turns menacingly towards* UNCLE VERNON.

HAGRID
Do you mean ter tell me, that this boy – this boy! – knows
nothin' abou' – about ANYTHING?

UNCLE VERNON
I forbid you to tell the boy anything more!

YOUNG HARRY
Tell me what?

HAGRID *looks at* UNCLE VERNON *and then at* YOUNG
HARRY.

HAGRID
Harry – yer a wizard – yeh changed everything. Yer the
most famous wizard in the whole world.

*And then right from the back of the room and whispering
around everyone, words said with an unmistakeable
voice. The voice of* VOLDEMORT . . .
Haaarry Potttter . . .

ACT ONE   SCENE NINE

HARRY AND GINNY POTTER'S HOUSE, BEDROOM

HARRY *wakes suddenly. Breathing deeply in the night.*
He waits a moment. Calming himself. And then he feels intense pain, in his forehead. In his scar. Around him Dark Magic moves.

GINNY
Harry ...

HARRY
It's fine. Go back to sleep.

GINNY
Lumos.

> *The room is filled with light from her wand.* HARRY *looks at her.*

A nightmare?

HARRY
Yes.

GINNY
About what?

HARRY
The Dursleys – well it started there – then it became something else.

> *Pause.* GINNY *looks at him – trying to work out where he is.*

GINNY

Do you want a Sleeping Draught?

HARRY

No. I'll be fine. Go back to sleep.

GINNY

You don't seem fine.

HARRY *says nothing.*

(Seeing his agitation.) It can't have been easy – with Amos Diggory.

HARRY

The anger I can cope with, the fact he's right is harder. Amos lost his son because of me—

GINNY

That doesn't seem particularly fair on yourself—

HARRY

—and there's nothing I can say – nothing I can say to anyone – unless it's the wrong thing of course.

GINNY *knows what – or rather who – he's referring to.*

GINNY

So that's what's upsetting you? The night before Hogwarts, it's never a good night if you don't want to go. Giving Al the blanket. It was a nice try.

HARRY

It went pretty badly wrong from there. I said some things Ginny ...

GINNY

I heard.

HARRY

And you're still talking to me?

GINNY

Because I know that when the time is right you'll say sorry. That you didn't mean it. That what you said concealed – other things. You can be honest with him Harry ... that's all he needs.

46

HARRY
I just wish he was more like James or Lily.

GINNY (*dryly*)
Yeah, maybe don't be that honest.

HARRY
No, I wouldn't change a thing about him ... but I can understand them and ...

GINNY
Albus is different and isn't that a good thing. And he can tell – you know – when you're putting on your Harry Potter front. He wants to see the real you.

HARRY
'The truth is a beautiful and terrible thing, and should therefore be treated with great caution.'

GINNY *looks at him, surprised.*

Dumbledore.

GINNY
A strange thing to say to a child.

HARRY
Not when you believe that child will have to die to save the world.

HARRY *gasps again – and does all he can not to touch his forehead.*

GINNY
Harry. What's wrong?

HARRY
Fine. I'm fine. I hear you. I'll try to be—

GINNY
Does your scar hurt?

HARRY
No. No. I'm fine. Now, Nox that and let's get some sleep.

GINNY
Harry. How long has it been since your scar hurt?

HARRY *turns to* GINNY, *his face says it all.*

HARRY
Twenty-two years.

———

ACT ONE   SCENE TEN

THE HOGWARTS EXPRESS

ALBUS *walks quickly along the busy train. He keeps his head down, trying to avoid attention.*

ROSE
   Albus, I've been looking for you ...

ALBUS
   Me? Why?

   ROSE *isn't sure how to phrase what she has to say.*

ROSE
   Albus, it's the start of the fourth year, and so the start of a new year for us. I want to be friends again.

ALBUS
   We never were friends.

ROSE
   That's harsh! You were my best friend when I was six!

ALBUS
   That was a long time ago.

   He makes to walk away, she pulls him into an empty compartment.

ROSE
   Have you heard the rumours? Big Ministry raid a few days ago. Your dad apparently was incredibly brave.

49

ALBUS

How do you always know about these things and I don't?

ROSE

Apparently he – the wizard they raided – Theodore Nott I
think – had all sorts of artefacts that broke all sorts of laws
including – and this has got them all gooey – an illegal
Time-Turner. And quite a superior one at that.

ALBUS looks at ROSE, everything falling into place.

ALBUS

A Time-Turner? My dad found a Time-Turner?

ROSE

Sh! Yes. I know. Great, right?

ALBUS

You're sure?

ROSE

Entirely.

ALBUS

Now I *have* to find Scorpius.

*He walks down the train. ROSE follows, still determined to
say her piece.*

ROSE

Albus!

ALBUS turns decisively.

ALBUS

Who's told you that you have to talk to me?

ROSE *(sprung)*

Okay, maybe your mum owled my dad – but only because
she's worried about you. And I just think—

ALBUS

Leave me alone, Rose.

*SCORPIUS is sitting in his usual compartment. ALBUS enters
first, ROSE still tailing him.*

SCORPIUS
Albus! Oh hello Rose, what do you smell of?

ROSE
What do I *smell* of?

SCORPIUS
No, I meant it as a nice thing. You smell like a mixture of fresh flowers and fresh – bread.

ROSE
Albus, I'm here, okay? If you need me.

SCORPIUS *(digging desperately)*
I mean, nice bread, good bread, bread ... what's wrong with bread?

> ROSE *walks away, shaking her head.*

ROSE
What's wrong with bread!

ALBUS
I've been looking for you everywhere ...

SCORPIUS
And now you've found me. Tada! I was hardly hiding. You know how I like to ... get on early. Stops people staring. Shouting. Writing 'son of Voldemort' on my trunk. That one never gets old. She really doesn't like me does she?

> ALBUS *hugs his friend. With fierceness. They hold for a beat.* SCORPIUS *is surprised by this.*

Okay. Hello. Um. Have we hugged before? Do we hug?

> *The two boys awkwardly dislocate.*

ALBUS
Just a slightly weird twenty-four hours.

SCORPIUS
What's happened in them?

ALBUS
I'll explain later. We have to get off this train.

There's the sound of whistles from off. The train starts moving.

SCORPIUS

Too late. The train is moving. Hogwarts ahoy!

ALBUS

Then we have to get off a moving train.

TROLLEY WITCH

Anything from the trolley, dears?

ALBUS opens a window and makes to climb out.

SCORPIUS

A moving magical train.

TROLLEY WITCH

Pumpkin Pasty? Cauldron Cake?

SCORPIUS

Albus Severus Potter, get that strange look out of your eye.

ALBUS

First question. What do you know about the Triwizard Tournament?

SCORPIUS *(happy)*

Ooooh, a quiz! Three schools pick three champions to compete in three tasks for one Cup. What's that got to do with anything?

ALBUS

You really are an enormous geek you know that?

SCORPIUS

Ya-huh.

ALBUS

Second question. Why has the Triwizard Tournament not been run in over twenty years?

SCORPIUS

The last competition included your dad and a boy called Cedric Diggory – they decided to win together but the Cup was a Portkey – and they were transported to Voldemort.

Cedric was killed. They cancelled the competition immediately after.

ALBUS

Good. Third question. Did Cedric need to be killed? Easy question, easy answer: No. The words Voldemort said were 'kill the spare'. The spare. He died only because he was with my father and my father couldn't save him – we can. A mistake has been made and we're going to right it. We're going to use a Time-Turner. We're going to bring him back.

SCORPIUS

Albus, for obvious reasons, I'm not a massive fan of Time-Turners . . .

ALBUS

When Amos Diggory asked for the Time-Turner my father denied they even existed. He lied to an old man who just wanted his son back – who just loved his son. And he did it because he didn't care . . . because he doesn't care. Everyone talks about all the brave things Dad did. But he made some mistakes too. Some big mistakes, in fact. I want to set one of those mistakes right. I want us to save Cedric.

SCORPIUS

Okay, whatever was holding your brain together seems to have snapped.

ALBUS

I'm going to do this, Scorpius. I need to do this. And you know as well as I do, I'll entirely mess it up if you don't come with me. Come on.

He grins. And then disappears ever up. SCORPIUS *hesitates for a moment. He makes a face. But he knows what he has to do – what he's going to do – he hoists himself up and disappears after* ALBUS.

ACT ONE   SCENE ELEVEN

THE HOGWARTS EXPRESS, ROOF

The wind whistles from all angles and it's a fierce wind at that as a determined ALBUS *and petrified* SCORPIUS *stand on the roof of a train.*

SCORPIUS
Okay, now we're on the roof of a train, it's fast, it's scary, this has been great, I feel like I've learnt a lot about me, something about you, but—

ALBUS
As I calculate it we should be approaching the viaduct soon and then it'll be a short hike to St Oswald's Home for Old Witches and Wizards . . .

SCORPIUS
The what? The where? Look, I am as excited as you are to be a rebel for the first time in my life – yay – train roof – fun – but now – oh.

SCORPIUS *sees something he doesn't want to see.*

ALBUS
The water will be an extremely useful back-up if our Cushioning Charm doesn't work.

SCORPIUS
Albus. The Trolley Witch.

ALBUS

You want a snack for the journey?

SCORPIUS

No. Albus. The Trolley Witch is coming towards us.

ALBUS

No, she can't be, we're on top of the train . . .

> SCORPIUS *points* ALBUS *in the right direction, and now he can see the* TROLLEY WITCH, *who approaches nonchalantly. Pushing her trolley.*

TROLLEY WITCH

Anything from the trolley, dears? Pumpkin Pasty? Chocolate Frog? Cauldron Cake?

ALBUS

Oh.

TROLLEY WITCH

People don't know much about me. They buy my Cauldron Cakes – but they never really notice me. I don't remember the last time someone asked my name.

ALBUS

What is your name?

TROLLEY WITCH

I've forgotten. All I can tell you is that when the Hogwarts Express first came to be – Ottaline Gambol herself offered me this job . . .

SCORPIUS

That's – a hundred and ninety years. You've been doing this job for a hundred and ninety years?

TROLLEY WITCH

These hands have made over six million Pumpkin Pasties. I've got quite good at them. But what people haven't noticed about my Pumpkin Pasties is how easily they transform into something else . . .

> *She picks up a Pumpkin Pasty. She throws it like a grenade. It explodes.*

And you won't believe what I can do with my Chocolate
Frogs. Never. Never. Have I let anyone off this train before
they reached their destination. Some have tried – Sirius
Black and his cronies, Fred and George Weasley. ALL
HAVE FAILED. BECAUSE THIS TRAIN – IT DOESN'T
LIKE PEOPLE GETTING OFF IT ...

The TROLLEY WITCH's *hands transfigure into very sharp
spikes. She smiles.*

So please retake your seats for the remainder of the journey.

ALBUS

You were right, Scorpius. This train is magical.

SCORPIUS

At this precise moment in time, I take no pleasure in being
right.

ALBUS

But I was also right – about the viaduct – that's water down
there, time to try the Cushioning Charm.

SCORPIUS

Albus, this is a bad idea.

ALBUS

Is it? (*He has a moment's hesitation, then he realises the time
for hesitation has passed.*) Too late now. Three. Two. One.
Molliare!

He incants as he jumps.

SCORPIUS

Albus ... Albus ...

*He looks down desperately after his friend. He looks
at the approaching* TROLLEY WITCH. *Her hair wild. Her
spikes particularly spiky.*

Well, as fun as you clearly look, I have to go after my friend.

He pinches his nose, he jumps after ALBUS, *incanting as
he goes.*

Molliare!

ACT ONE   SCENE TWELVE

MINISTRY OF MAGIC, GRAND MEETING ROOM

The stage is flooded with wizards and witches. They rattle and chatter like all true wizards and witches can. Amongst them, GINNY, DRACO *and* RON. *Above them, on a stage,* HERMIONE *and* HARRY.

HERMIONE

Order. Order. Do I have to conjure silence? (*She pulls silence from the crowd using her wand.*) Good. Welcome to this Extraordinary General Meeting. I'm so pleased so many of you could make it. The wizarding world has been living in peace now for many years. It's twenty-two years since we defeated Voldemort at the Battle of Hogwarts and I'm delighted to say there is a new generation being brought up having known only the slightest conflict. Until now. Harry?

HARRY

Voldemort's allies have been showing movement for a few months now. We've followed trolls making their way across Europe, giants starting to cross the seas, and the werewolves – well, I'm distressed to say we lost sight of them some weeks ago. We don't know where they're going or who's encouraged them to move – but we are aware they are moving – and we are concerned what it might mean. So we're asking – if anyone has seen anything? Felt anything?

If you could raise a wand, we will hear everyone speak.
Professor McGonagall – thank you.

PROFESSOR MCGONAGALL
It did look like the Potions stores had been interfered with
when we returned from summer break, but not a huge
amount of ingredients were missing, some Boomslang skin
and lacewing flies, nothing on the Restricted Register. We
put it down to Peeves.

HERMIONE
Thank you, Professor. We shall investigate. (*She looks
around the room.*) Nobody else? Fine, and – gravest of all –
and this hasn't been the case since Voldemort – Harry's
scar is hurting again.

DRACO
Voldemort is dead, Voldemort is gone.

HERMIONE
Yes, Draco, Voldemort is dead but these things all lead us
to think that there is a possibility that Voldemort – or some
trace of Voldemort – might be back.

This gets a reaction.

HARRY
Now this is difficult but we have to ask it to rule it out.
Those of you with a Dark Mark . . . have you felt anything?
Even a twinge?

DRACO
Back to being prejudiced against those with a Dark Mark
are we, Potter?

HERMIONE
No, Draco. Harry is simply trying to—

DRACO
You know what this is about? Harry just wants his face back
in the newspapers again. We've had rumours of Voldemort
coming back from the *Daily Prophet* once a year every
year—

HARRY

None of those rumours came from me!

DRACO

Really? Doesn't your wife edit the *Daily Prophet*?

GINNY steps towards him, outraged.

GINNY

The sports pages!

HERMIONE

Draco. Harry brought this matter to the attention of the Ministry . . . and I, as Minister for Magic—

DRACO

A vote you only won because you are his friend.

RON is held back by GINNY as he charges at DRACO.

RON

Do you want a smack in the mouth?

DRACO

Face it – his celebrity impacts upon you all. And how better to get everyone whispering the Potter name again than with (*he does an impression of HARRY*) 'my scar is hurting, my scar is hurting'. And do you know what this all means – that the gossipmongers once again have an opportunity to defame my son with these ridiculous rumours about his parentage.

HARRY

Draco, no one is saying this has anything to do with Scorpius . . .

DRACO

Well, I, for one, think this meeting a sham. And I'm leaving.

He walks out. Others start to disperse after him.

HERMIONE

No. That's not the way . . . come back. We need a strategy.

ACT ONE   SCENE THIRTEEN

ST OSWALD'S HOME FOR OLD WITCHES AND WIZARDS

This is chaos. This is magic. This is St Oswald's Home for Old Witches and Wizards and it is as wonderful as you might hope.

Zimmer frames are conjured into life, knitting wool is enchanted into chaos, and male nurses are made to dance the tango.

These are people relieved of the burden of having to do magic for a reason – instead, these witches and wizards do magic for fun. And what fun they have.

ALBUS *and* SCORPIUS *enter, looking around themselves, amused, and – let's face it – slightly scared.*

ALBUS *and* SCORPIUS
Um, excuse me . . . Excuse me. EXCUSE ME!

SCORPIUS
Okay, so this place is wild.

ALBUS
We're looking for Amos Diggory.

> *There is suddenly total silence. Everything is instantly still. And slightly depressed.*

WOOL WOMAN
And what'you boys want with that miserable old sod?

> DELPHI *appears with a smile.*

DELPHI

Albus? Albus! You came? How wonderful! Come and say
hello to Amos!

ACT ONE   SCENE FOURTEEN

ST OSWALD'S HOME FOR OLD WITCHES AND WIZARDS, AMOS'S ROOM

AMOS *looks at* SCORPIUS *and* ALBUS, *irritated.* DELPHI *watches the three of them.*

AMOS
So let me get this straight. You overhear a conversation – a conversation which was not meant for you to overhear – and you decide, without prompting – in fact, without leave – to interfere, and interfere hard, in someone else's business.

ALBUS
My father lied to you – I know he did – they do have a Time-Turner.

AMOS
Of course they do. You can move along now.

ALBUS
What? No. We're here to help.

AMOS
Help? What use could a pair of undersized teenagers be for me?

ALBUS
My father proved you don't have to be grown up to change the wizarding world.

AMOS
So I should allow you to get involved because you're a
Potter? Relying on your famous name are you?

ALBUS
No!

AMOS
A Potter who is in Slytherin house – yes, I've read about
you – and who brings a Malfoy with him to visit me – a
Malfoy who may be a Voldemort? Who's to say you're not
involved in Dark Magic?

ALBUS
But—

AMOS
Your information was obvious but the confirmation is
useful. Your father did lie. Now leave. The pair of you. And
stop wasting my time.

ALBUS (with power and strength)
No, you need to listen to me, you said it yourself – how
much blood is on my father's hands. Let me help you
change that. Let me help correct one of his mistakes. Trust
me.

AMOS (his voice raised)
Did you not hear me, boy? I see no reason to trust you. So
go. Now. Before I *make* you leave.

He raises his wand ominously. ALBUS *looks at the wand –
he deflates –* AMOS *has crushed him.*

SCORPIUS
Come on mate, if there's one thing we're good at, it's
knowing where we're not wanted.

ALBUS *is reluctant to leave.* SCORPIUS *pulls him by the
arm. He turns and they walk away.*

DELPHI
I can think of one reason why you should trust them,
Uncle.

They stop.

They're the only ones volunteering to help. They're prepared to bravely put themselves at risk to return your son to your side. In fact, I'm pretty sure they put themselves at risk even getting here . . .

AMOS

This is Cedric we're talking about . . .

DELPHI

And – didn't you say yourself – having someone inside Hogwarts might be a *massive* advantage?

DELPHI kisses the top of AMOS's head. AMOS looks at DELPHI, and then turns to look at the boys.

AMOS

Why? Why do you want to put yourself at risk? What's in it for you?

ALBUS

I know what it is to be the spare. Your son didn't deserve to be killed, Mr Diggory. We can help you get him back.

AMOS *(finally showing emotion)*

My son – my son was the best thing that ever happened to me – and you're right it was an injustice – a gross injustice – if you're serious . . .

ALBUS

We're deadly serious.

AMOS

This is going to be dangerous.

ALBUS

We know.

SCORPIUS

Do we?

AMOS

Delphi – perhaps if you were prepared to accompany them?

DELPHI

If that would make you happy, Uncle.

She smiles at ALBUS, *he smiles back.*

AMOS
You do understand even getting the Time-Turner will risk your lives.

ALBUS
We're ready to put our lives at risk.

SCORPIUS
Are we?

AMOS *(gravely)*
I hope you have it in you.

ACT ONE   SCENE FIFTEEN

HARRY AND GINNY POTTER'S HOUSE, KITCHEN

HARRY, RON, HERMIONE *and* GINNY *sit eating together.*

HERMIONE
I've told Draco again and again – no one in the Ministry is saying anything about Scorpius. The rumours aren't coming from us.

GINNY
I wrote to him – after he lost Astoria – to ask if there's anything we could do. I thought maybe – as he was such a good friend to Albus – maybe Scorpius might want to stay over part of the Christmas break or . . . My owl came back with a letter containing one simple sentence: 'Tell your husband to refute these allegations about my son once and for all.'

HERMIONE
He's obsessed.

GINNY
He's a mess – a grieving mess.

RON
And I'm sorry for his loss, but when he accuses Hermione of . . . well . . . (*he looks across at* HARRY) Oi droopy drawers, like I say to her all the time, it could be nothing.

HERMIONE
Her?

RON
The trolls could be going to a party, the giants to a wedding, you could be getting bad dreams because you're worried about Albus, and your scar could be hurting because you're getting old.

HARRY
Getting old? Thanks, mate.

RON
Honestly, every time I sit down now I make an 'ooof' noise. An 'ooof'. And my feet – the trouble I'm having with my feet – I could write songs about the pain my feet give me – maybe your scar is like that.

GINNY
You talk a lot of rubbish.

RON
I consider it my speciality. That and my range of Skiving Snackboxes. And my love for all of you. Even Skinny Ginny.

GINNY
If you don't behave, Ronald Weasley, I will tell Mum.

RON
You wouldn't.

HERMIONE
If some part of Voldemort survived, in whatever form, we need to be prepared. And I'm scared.

GINNY
I'm scared too.

RON
Nothing scares me. Apart from Mum.

HERMIONE
I mean it, Harry, I will not be Cornelius Fudge on this one. I will not stick my head in the sand. And I don't care how unpopular that makes me with Draco Malfoy.

RON

You never really were one for popularity were you?

HERMIONE shoots RON a withering look as she aims to hit him but RON jumps out of the way.

Missed.

GINNY wallops RON. RON winces.

Hit. A very solid hit.

Suddenly an owl is in the room. It swoops in low and drops a letter on Harry's plate.

HERMIONE

Bit late for an owl isn't it?

Harry opens the letter. Surprised.

HARRY

It's from Professor McGonagall.

GINNY

What does it say?

HARRY's face drops.

HARRY

Ginny, it's Albus – Albus and Scorpius – they never made it to school. They're missing!

ACT ONE   SCENE SIXTEEN

WHITEHALL, CELLAR

SCORPIUS, *flanked by* ALBUS *and* DELPHI, *is squinting at a bottle.*

SCORPIUS
So we just take it?

ALBUS
Scorpius, do I really need to explain to you – uber geek and
Potions expert – what Polyjuice does? Thanks to Delphi's
brilliant preparation work, we are going to take this potion
and be transformed, and thus disguised we will be able to
enter the Ministry of Magic.

SCORPIUS
Okay, two points, one, is it painful?

DELPHI
Very – as I understand it.

SCORPIUS
Thank you. Good to know. Second point – do either of you
know what Polyjuice tastes of? Because I've heard it tastes
of fish, and if it does I will just vomit it back up. Fish doesn't
agree with me. Never has. Never will.

DELPHI
Consider us warned. (*She takes a breath and knocks back
the potion.*) It doesn't taste of fish. (*She begins to transform.
It's agonising.*) Actually it tastes quite pleasant, yum. It is

painful but ... (*She burps, loudly.*) Take it back. There is a –
slight – (*She burps again and turns into* HERMIONE.) Slight –
overpowering – fishy residue.

ALBUS

Okay, that's – wow!

SCORPIUS

Double wow!

DELPHI/HERMIONE

This really doesn't feel how I – I even sound like her! Triple
wow!

ALBUS

Right. Me next.

SCORPIUS

No. No way, José. If we're doing this, we're doing it (*he puts
on a pair of familiar-looking glasses with a smile*) together.

ALBUS

Three. Two. One.

They swallow.

No, that's good (*he's racked with pain*). That's less good.

They both start to transform and it's agonising.

ALBUS *turns into* RON, SCORPIUS *into* HARRY.

The two look at each other. There's a silence.

ALBUS/RON

This is going to be slightly weird isn't it?

SCORPIUS/HARRY (*full of drama – he's really enjoying this*)
Go to your room. Go straight to your room. You've been an
incredibly awful and bad son.

ALBUS/RON (*with a laugh*)
Scorpius ...

SCORPIUS/HARRY (*tossing his cloak over his shoulder*)
It was your idea – I be him and you be Ron! I just want
to have a little fun before I ... (*And then he burps loudly.*)
Okay, so that's utterly horrible.

ALBUS/RON
> You know, he hides it well, but Uncle Ron's got a bit of a
> gut growing.

DELPHI/HERMIONE
> We should go – don't you think?

> *They emerge on to the street. They enter a telephone box.*
> *They dial 62442.*

TELEPHONE BOX
> Welcome, Harry Potter. Welcome, Hermione Granger.
> Welcome, Ron Weasley.

> *They smile as the telephone box disappears into the floor.*

ACT ONE   SCENE SEVENTEEN

MINISTRY OF MAGIC, MEETING ROOM

HARRY, HERMIONE, GINNY *and* DRACO *pace around a small room. All four of them are wracked with worry.*

DRACO

Have we searched thoroughly beside the tracks?

HARRY

My department have searched once and are searching again.

DRACO

And the Trolley Witch is not able to tell us anything useful?

HERMIONE

The Trolley Witch is furious. She keeps talking about letting down Ottaline Gambol. She prides herself on her Hogwarts delivery record.

GINNY

Have there been any instances of magic reported by the Muggles?

HERMIONE

None so far. I have made the Muggle Prime Minister aware and he is filing what is known as a misper. Sounds like a spell. It isn't.

DRACO

So now we're relying on Muggles to find our children? Have we told them about Harry's scar too?

HERMIONE *tries to puncture the atmosphere that is developing.*

HERMIONE

We're merely asking the Muggles to help. And who knows how Harry's scar might be involved but it's certainly a matter we're taking seriously. Our Aurors are currently investigating anyone involved in Dark Magic and—

DRACO

This is *not* Death Eater-related.

HERMIONE

I'm not sure I share your confidence . . .

DRACO

I'm not confident, I'm right. The sort of cretins pursuing Dark Magic now. My son is a Malfoy, they wouldn't dare.

HARRY

Unless there's something new out there, something to—

GINNY

I agree with Draco – if this is a kidnap – taking Albus I understand, taking them both . . .

HARRY *locks eyes with* GINNY, *it becomes clear what she wants him to say.*

DRACO

And Scorpius is a follower not a leader despite everything I've tried to instil in him. So it's undoubtedly Albus who got him from that train and my question is, where would he take him?

GINNY

Harry, they've run away, you and I know it.

DRACO *notices the couple staring at each other. He knows something is being communicated.*

73

PART ONE

DRACO
Do you? Know it? What aren't you telling us?

There's a silence.

Whatever information you're concealing, I recommend you share it now.

HARRY
Albus and I had an argument, the day before last.

DRACO
And ...

HARRY *hesitates and then makes brave eye contact with* DRACO.

HARRY
And I told him that there were times when I wished he weren't my son.

There's another silence. A profoundly powerful one. And then DRACO *takes a dangerous step towards* HARRY.

DRACO
If anything happens to Scorpius ...

GINNY *steps in between* DRACO *and* HARRY.

GINNY
Don't throw around threats Draco, please don't do that.

DRACO *(roar)*
My son is missing!

GINNY *(an equal roar)*
So is mine!

He meets her look. There's real emotion in this room.

DRACO *(lip curling, every inch his father)*
If you need gold ... everything the Malfoys have ... he's my sole heir ... he's my – only family.

HERMIONE
The Ministry has plenty in reserve, thank you Draco.

74

DRACO *makes to leave. He stops. He looks at* HARRY.

DRACO
I don't care what you did or who you saved, you are a constant curse on my family, Harry Potter.

ACT ONE   SCENE EIGHTEEN

MINISTRY OF MAGIC, CORRIDOR

SCORPIUS/HARRY
And you're sure it's in there?

A GUARD *walks past.* SCORPIUS/HARRY *and* DELPHI/
HERMIONE *try to affect performances.*

Yes Minister, I definitely think this is a matter for the
Ministry to ponder at length, yes.

GUARD (*with a nod*)
Minister.

DELPHI/HERMIONE
Let's ponder it together.

The GUARD *walks on, they let out a sigh of relief.*

It was my uncle's idea to use the Veritaserum – we slipped it
into a visiting Ministry official's drink. He told us that the
Time-Turner had been kept and even told us where – the
office of the Minister for Magic herself.

She indicates a door. Suddenly they hear a noise.

HERMIONE (*from off*)
Harry ... we should talk about it ...

HARRY (*from off*)
There's nothing to talk about.

DELPHI/HERMIONE
Oh no.

ALBUS/RON
Hermione. And Dad.

The panic is instant and infectious.

SCORPIUS/HARRY
Okay. Hiding places. No hiding places. Anyone know any
Invisibility Charms?

DELPHI/HERMIONE
Do we go – in her office?

ALBUS/RON
She'll be coming to her office.

DELPHI/HERMIONE
There's nowhere else.

She tries the door. She tries it again.

HERMIONE (*from off*)
If you don't talk to me or Ginny about it . . .

SCORPIUS/HARRY
Stand back. Alohomora!

*He aims his wand at the door. The door swings open. He
grins – delighted.*

Albus. Block her. It has to be you.

HARRY (*from off*)
What is there to say?

ALBUS/RON
Me. Why?

DELPHI/HERMIONE
Well, it can't be either of us can it? We *are* them.

HERMIONE (*from off*)
What you said was obviously wrong – but – there are more
factors at play here than—

ALBUS/RON
But I can't . . . I can't . . .

There's a small kerfuffle and then ALBUS/RON *ends up standing outside the door as* HERMIONE *and* HARRY *enter from off.*

HARRY

Hermione, I'm grateful for your concern but there's no need—

HERMIONE

Ron?

ALBUS/RON

Surprise!!!

HERMIONE

What are you doing here?

ALBUS/RON

Does a man need an excuse to see his wife?

He kisses HERMIONE *firmly.*

HARRY

I should go . . .

HERMIONE

Harry. My point is whatever Draco says – the things you said to Albus . . . I don't think it'll do any of us any good for you to dwell on it . . .

ALBUS/RON

Oh, you're talking about how Harry said sometimes he wished I— (*he corrects himself*) Albus weren't his son.

HERMIONE

Ron!

ALBUS/RON

Better out than in, that's what I say . . .

HERMIONE

He'll know . . . we all say stuff we don't mean. He knows that.

ALBUS/RON

But what if sometimes we say stuff we do mean . . . what then?

HERMIONE
Ron, now's not the time, honestly.

ALBUS/RON
Of course it isn't. Bye, bye darling.

ALBUS/RON *watches her go, hopeful she'll walk past her office and away. But of course she doesn't. He runs to block her before she enters through her door. He blocks her once, and then blocks her again, swinging his hips to do so.*

HERMIONE
Why are you blocking the entrance to my office?

ALBUS/RON
I'm not. Blocking. Anything.

She again makes for the door, he blocks her again.

HERMIONE
You are. Let me into my room, Ron.

HERMIONE *tries to dodge past him.*

ALBUS/RON
Let's have another baby.

HERMIONE
What?

ALBUS/RON
Or if not another baby, a holiday. I want a baby or a holiday and I'm going to insist on it. Shall we talk about it later, honey? Maybe with a drink in the Leaky Cauldron? Love you.

HERMIONE *thinks, she stares at him suspiciously and then looks again at her door. She relents.*

HERMIONE
If there's another stink pellet in there then Merlin won't help you. Fine. We're due to update the Muggles anyway.

She exits. HARRY *exits with her.*

ALBUS/RON *turns towards the door. She re-enters, this time, alone.*

A baby – OR – a holiday? Some days you are off the scale you know that?

ALBUS/RON
It's why you married me isn't it? My puckish sense of fun.

She exits again. He starts to open the door but again she re-enters, he slams it closed.

HERMIONE
I can taste fish. I told you to stay away from those fish finger sandwiches.

ALBUS/RON
Right you are.

She exits. He checks she's gone and the relief floods out of him as he opens the door.

ACT ONE   SCENE NINETEEN

MINISTRY OF MAGIC, HERMIONE'S OFFICE

SCORPIUS/HARRY *and* DELPHI/HERMIONE *are waiting on the other side of* HERMIONE's *office door as* ALBUS/RON *enters – he slumps, exhausted.*

ALBUS/RON
> This is all too weird.

DELPHI/HERMIONE
> You were impressive. Good blocking action.

SCORPIUS/HARRY
> I don't know whether to high-five you or frown at you for kissing your aunt about five hundred times!

ALBUS/RON
> Ron's an affectionate guy. I was trying to distract her, Scorpius. I did distract her.

SCORPIUS/HARRY
> And then there's what your dad said . . .

DELPHI/HERMIONE
> Boys . . . she will be back – we don't have long.

ALBUS/RON *(to* SCORPIUS/HARRY*)*
> You heard that?

DELPHI/HERMIONE
> Where would Hermione hide a Time-Turner? (*She looks around the room and sees the bookcases.*) Search the bookcases.

They start to search. SCORPIUS/HARRY *looks at his friend, concerned.*

SCORPIUS/HARRY
Why didn't you tell me?

ALBUS/RON
My dad says he wishes I weren't his son. Hardly a conversation starter is it?

SCORPIUS/HARRY *tries to work out what to say.*

SCORPIUS/HARRY
I know the – Voldemort thing isn't – true – and – you know – but sometimes, I think I can see my dad thinking: how did I produce this?

ALBUS/RON
Still better than my dad. I'm pretty sure he spends most of his time thinking: how can I give him back?

DELPHI/HERMIONE *tries to pull* SCORPIUS/HARRY *towards the bookcases.*

DELPHI/HERMIONE
Maybe if we could concentrate on the matter at hand.

SCORPIUS/HARRY
My point is – there's a reason – we're friends, Albus – a reason we found each other, you know? And whatever this – adventure is about . . .

Then he spots a book on the shelf that makes him frown.

Have you seen the books on these shelves? There are some serious books here. Banned books. Cursed books.

ALBUS/RON
How to distract Scorpius from difficult emotional issues. Take him to a library.

SCORPIUS/HARRY

All the books from the Restricted Section and then some.
*Magick Moste Evile, Fifteenth-Century Fiends. Sonnets of a
Sorcerer* – that's not even allowed in Hogwarts!

ALBUS/RON

Shadows and Spirits. The Nightshade Guide to Necromancy.

DELPHI/HERMIONE

They are quite something aren't they . . .

ALBUS/RON

*The True History of the Opal Fire. The Imperius Curse and
How to Abuse it.*

SCORPIUS/HARRY

And lookee here. Whoah. *My Eyes and How to See Past
Them* by Sybill Trelawney. A book on divination. Hermione
Granger hates divination. This is fascinating. This is a
find . . .

*He pulls the book from the shelf. And it falls open. And
speaks.*

BOOK

The first is the fourth, a disappointing mark
You'll find it in parked but not in park.

SCORPIUS/HARRY

Okay. A book that talks. Bit weird.

BOOK

The second is the less fair of those who walk on two legs.
Grubby, hairy a disease of the egg.
And the third is both a mountain to climb and a route to
take.

ALBUS/RON

It's a riddle. It's giving us a riddle.

BOOK

A turn in the city, a glide through a lake.

DELPHI/HERMIONE

What have you done?

SCORPIUS/HARRY

I, uh, I opened a book. Something which has – in all my years on this planet – never been a particularly dangerous activity.

The books reach out and grab ALBUS/RON. *He only just eludes their grasp.*

ALBUS/RON

What is that?

DELPHI/HERMIONE *(excited)*

She's weaponised it. She's weaponised her library. This is where the Time-Turner will be. Solve the riddle and we'll find it.

ALBUS/RON

The first is a fourth. You'll find it in parked, not in park. Ed – De—

SCORPIUS/HARRY

The second is a disease of the egg, the less fair of those who walk on two legs . . .

DELPHI/HERMIONE *(effusively)*

Men! De – men – tors. We need to find a book on Dementors. *(She approaches the bookcase and then is surprised as it tries to swallow her.)* Albus!

ALBUS/RON *rushes towards the bookcase but is too late as she's swallowed whole.*

ALBUS/RON

Delphi! What is going on?

SCORPIUS/HARRY

Concentrate, Albus. Do what she said. Find a book on Dementors and be very careful.

ALBUS/RON

Here. *Dominating Dementors: A True History of Azkaban.*

The book flies open and swings dangerously at SCORPIUS/
HARRY, *who has to dodge out of the way. He falls hard
against a bookcase which attempts to consume him.*

BOOK
I was born in a cage
But smashed it with rage
The Gaunt inside me
Riddled me free
Of that which would stop me to be.

ALBUS/RON
Voldemort.

DELPHI plunges through the books, back as herself.

DELPHI
Work faster!

She's pulled back in screaming.

ALBUS/RON
Delphi! Delphi!

He tries to grab her hand, but she's gone.

SCORPIUS/HARRY
She'd become herself again – did you notice?

ALBUS/RON
No! Because I was more worried about her being eaten by a
bookcase! Find. Something. Anything on him.

He finds a book.

The Heir of Slytherin? Do you think?

*He pulls the book from the shelf, it pulls back, he tries
desperately to fight it, but* ALBUS/RON *is consumed by the
bookcase.*

SCORPIUS/HARRY
Albus? Albus!!

Before SCORPIUS/HARRY *can reach him,* ALBUS/RON *is gone. He thinks a moment, full of doubt, and then realises this is his job to finish now.*

Okay. Not that. Voldemort. Voldemort. Voldemort.

He scans the shelves.

Marvolo: *The Truth,* this must be ...

He pulls it open. Again it swings away, revealing a splintering light, and a deeper voice than previously heard.

BOOK
I am the creature you have not seen
I am you. I am me. The echo unforeseen.
Sometimes in front, sometimes behind,
A constant companion, for we are entwined.

ALBUS *emerges from the books. As himself again.*

SCORPIUS/HARRY
Albus ...

He tries to grab him. But the bookcase is too strong.

ALBUS
No. Just – THIIIIINK.

ALBUS *is violently pulled back into the bookcase.*

SCORPIUS/HARRY
But I can't ... an invisible echo, what is that? The only thing I'm good at is thinking and when I need to think – I can't.

The books pull him inside them; he's powerless. This is terrifying.
There's silence. All of our three have been consumed. There's nothing.
Then BANG – a shower of books are released from the

86

bookcase – and SCORPIUS *re-emerges. Smashing the books aside.*

SCORPIUS
No! You don't! Sybill Trelawney. No!!!

He looks around, sunk but full of energy.

This is all wrong. Albus? Can you hear me? All this for a frigging Time-Turner. Think, Scorpius. Think.

Books try and grab him but he eludes their grasp.

A constant companion. Sometimes behind. Sometimes in front. Hang on. I've missed it. Shadow. You're a shadow. *Shadows and Spirits.* It must be …

He climbs up the bookcase, which is horrifying as it rises up at him. Grabbing at him with his every step.
He pulls the book from the shelf. It comes out and the noise and chaos suddenly stop.

Is that—

Suddenly there's a smashing and ALBUS *and* DELPHI *fall out of the shelves and down to the floor.*

We beat it! We beat the library!

He raises his hands in triumph as ALBUS *anxiously looks at* DELPHI.

ALBUS
Delphi, are you … ?

DELPHI
Wow. Quite a ride.

ALBUS *notices the book* SCORPIUS *is holding to his chest.*

ALBUS
Is that …? Scorpius? What's inside that book?

DELPHI
I think we should find out don't you?

87

SCORPIUS *opens the book. In the centre of it – a spinning Time-Turner.*

Wow.

SCORPIUS

We've found the Time-Turner – I never thought we'd get this far.

ALBUS

Mate, now we've got this, the next stop is saving Cedric. Our journey has only just begun.

SCORPIUS

Only just begun and it's almost half-killed us. Good. This is going to be good.

Whispers rise to a roar. And we cut to black.

INTERVAL

PART ONE

ACT TWO

ACT TWO   SCENE ONE

DREAM, PRIVET DRIVE, CUPBOARD UNDER THE STAIRS

YOUNG HARRY, *asleep in the cupboard under the stairs, is having a nightmare. He tosses and turns as he feels a dark presence around him.*

AUNT PETUNIA *(offstage)*
> Harry. Harry. These pots aren't clean. THESE POTS ARE A DISGRACE. HARRY POTTER. Wake up.

> YOUNG HARRY *wakes to see* AUNT PETUNIA *bearing down on him.*

YOUNG HARRY
> Aunt Petunia. What time is it?

AUNT PETUNIA
> Time enough. You know, when we agreed to take you in, we hoped we could improve you – build you – make you a decent human being. So I suppose it's only ourselves we've got to blame that you've turned out – such a limp disappointment.

YOUNG HARRY
> I try—

AUNT PETUNIA
> Trying is not succeeding, though, is it? There are grease

smears on the glasses. There are scuff marks on the pots. Now get up and go to the kitchen and get scrubbing.

He gets out of bed. There's a wet smear down the back of his trousers.

Oh no. Oh no. What have you done? You've wet the bed, again.

She pulls back the covers.

This is very unacceptable.

YOUNG HARRY
I'm ... sorry, I think I was having a nightmare.

AUNT PETUNIA
You disgusting boy. Only animals wet themselves. Animals and disgusting little boys.

YOUNG HARRY
It was about my mum and dad. I think I saw them – I think I saw them – die?

AUNT PETUNIA
And why would I have the slightest bit of interest in that?

YOUNG HARRY
There was a man shouting Adkava Ad-something Acabra – Ad – and the noise of a snake hissing. I could hear my mum scream.

AUNT PETUNIA *takes a moment to reset herself.*

AUNT PETUNIA
If you were really reliving their death, all you'd hear would be a screech of brakes and a horrific thud. Your parents died in a car accident. You know that. I don't think your mother had even time to scream. Lord spare you the details more than that. Now strip those sheets, get in the kitchen and get scrubbing. I don't want to have to tell you again.

She exits with a bang.
And YOUNG HARRY *is left holding the sheets.*

And the stage contorts and trees rise as the dream twists into something else entirely.

Suddenly, from within the trees ALBUS *appears and stands looking at* YOUNG HARRY.

And then he's pulled hard away.

To be replaced by Parseltongue whispers reverberating around the theatre.

He's coming. He's coming.

Words said with an unmistakeable voice. The voice of VOLDEMORT . . .

Haaarry Pottttter . . .

ACT TWO SCENE TWO

HARRY AND GINNY POTTER'S HOUSE, STAIRCASE

HARRY *wakes in the darkness, breathing deeply. His exhaustion palpable, his fear overwhelming.*

HARRY
Lumos.

GINNY *enters, surprised by the light.*

GINNY
Okay ... ?

HARRY
I was sleeping.

GINNY
You were.

HARRY
You weren't. Any – news? Any owls or ... ?

GINNY *looks at him, tired and scared.*

GINNY
None.

HARRY
I was dreaming – I was under the stairs and then I – I heard him – Voldemort – so clearly.

GINNY
Voldemort?

HARRY
And then I saw – Albus. In red – he was wearing
Durmstrang robes.

GINNY
Durmstrang robes?

HARRY *thinks*.

HARRY
Ginny, I think I know where he is . . .

———

ACT TWO SCENE THREE

HOGWARTS, HEADMISTRESS'S OFFICE

HARRY *and* GINNY *stand in* PROFESSOR MCGONAGALL's *office.*

PROFESSOR MCGONAGALL
And we don't know where in the Forbidden Forest?

HARRY
I haven't had a dream like it for years. But Albus was there.
I know he was.

GINNY
We need to get searching as quickly as possible.

PROFESSOR MCGONAGALL
I can give you Professor Longbottom – his knowledge of
plants might be useful – and—

Suddenly there is a rumble in the chimney. PROFESSOR
MCGONAGALL *looks at it, concerned. Then* HERMIONE
tumbles out.

HERMIONE
Is it true? Can I help?

PROFESSOR MCGONAGALL
Minister – this is quite unexpected . . .

GINNY
That may be my fault – I persuaded them to put out
an emergency edition of the *Daily Prophet*. Asking for
volunteers.

PROFESSOR MCGONAGALL
Right. Very sensible. I expect . . . there will be quite a few.

RON *bursts in. Covered in soot. Wearing a gravy-stained
dinner napkin.*

RON
Have I missed anything – I couldn't work out which Floo
to travel to. Ended up in the kitchen somehow. (HERMIONE
glares as he pulls the napkin off himself.) What?

*Suddenly there is another rumble in the chimney and
DRACO comes down hard, surrounded by cascading soot
and dust.*

*Everyone looks at him, surprised. He stands and brushes
the soot off himself.*

DRACO
Sorry about your floor, Minerva.

PROFESSOR MCGONAGALL
I dare say it's my fault for owning a chimney.

HARRY
Quite a surprise to see you, Draco. I thought you didn't
believe in my dreams.

DRACO
I don't, but I do trust your luck. Harry Potter is always
where the action is at. And I need my son back with me
and safe.

GINNY
Then let's get to the Forbidden Forest and find them both.

ACT TWO   SCENE FOUR

EDGE OF THE FORBIDDEN FOREST

ALBUS *and* DELPHI *face each other, holding wands.*

ALBUS
Expelliarmus!

> DELPHI'*s wand flies through the air.*

DELPHI
You're getting it now. You're good at this.

> *She takes her wand back from him.*
> *In a posh voice.*

'You're a positively disarming young man.'

ALBUS
Expelliarmus!

> *Her wand flies back again.*

DELPHI
And we have a winner.

> *The two high-five.*

ALBUS
I've never been good at spells.

SCORPIUS *appears at the back of the stage. He looks at his friend talking to a girl – and part of him likes it and part of him doesn't.*

DELPHI

I was rubbish – and then something clicked. And it will for you too. Not that I'm a super witch or anything but I think you're becoming quite some wizard, Albus Potter.

ALBUS

Then you should stick around – teach me more—

DELPHI

Of course I'm sticking around, we're friends aren't we?

ALBUS

Yes. Yes. Definitely friends. Definitely.

DELPHI

Great. Wizzo!

SCORPIUS

What's wizzo?

SCORPIUS *steps forward decisively.*

ALBUS

Cracked the spell. I mean, it's pretty basic, but I was – well, I cracked it.

SCORPIUS *(over-enthusiastic, trying to join in)*

And I've found our way through to the school. Listen, are we sure this will work . . .

DELPHI

Yes!

ALBUS

It's a brilliant plan. The secret to not getting Cedric killed is to stop him winning the Triwizard Tournament. If he doesn't win, he can't be killed.

SCORPIUS

And I understand that but . . .

ALBUS

So we just need to mess up his chances supremely badly in task one. The first task is getting a golden egg from a dragon – how did Cedric distract the dragon—

DELPHI *puts her hand in the air.* ALBUS *grins and points at her. These two are getting on really well now.*

Diggory.

DELPHI

—by transfiguring a stone into a dog.

ALBUS

—well, a little Expelliarmus and he won't be able to do that.

SCORPIUS *isn't enjoying the* DELPHI-ALBUS *double act.*

SCORPIUS

Okay, two points, first point we're certain the dragon won't kill him?

DELPHI

It's always two points with him isn't it? Of course it won't. This is Hogwarts. They won't let damage happen to any of the champions.

SCORPIUS

Okay, second *point* – more significant *point* – we're going back without any knowledge of whether we can travel back afterwards. Which is exciting. Maybe we should just – try going back an hour, say, first and then ...

DELPHI

I'm sorry, Scorpius, we've no time to waste. Waiting here this close to the school is just too dangerous – I'm sure they'll be looking for you and ...

ALBUS

She's right.

DELPHI

Now, you're going to need to wear these—

She pulls out two large paper bags. The boys pull out
robes from them.

ALBUS

But these are Durmstrang robes.

DELPHI

My uncle's idea. If you are in Hogwarts robes people will
expect to know who you are. But there are two other
schools competing at the Triwizard Tournament – and if
you're in Durmstrang robes – well, you can fade into the
background, can't you?

ALBUS

Good thinking! Hang on, where are your robes?

DELPHI

Albus, I'm flattered, but I don't think I can pretend to be
a student, do you? I'll just keep in the background, and
pretend to be a – ooh, maybe I could pretend to be a dragon
tamer. You're doing all the spell stuff anyway.

SCORPIUS *looks at her and then at* ALBUS.

SCORPIUS

You shouldn't come.

DELPHI

What?

SCORPIUS

You're right. We don't need you for the spell. And if you
can't wear student robes – you're too big a risk. Sorry,
Delphi, you shouldn't come.

DELPHI

But I have to – he's my cousin. Albus?

ALBUS

I think he's right. I'm sorry.

DELPHI

What?

ALBUS

We won't mess up.

DELPHI

But without me – you won't be able to work the
Time-Turner.

SCORPIUS

You taught us how to use the Time-Turner.

DELPHI is really upset.

DELPHI

No. I won't let you do this . . .

ALBUS

You told your uncle to trust us. Now it's your turn. The
school is close now. We should leave you here.

*DELPHI looks at them both and takes a deep breath. She
nods to herself and smiles.*

DELPHI

Then go. But – just know this . . . today you get an
opportunity few are given – today you get to change
history – to change time itself. But more than all that,
today you get the chance to give an old man his son back.

*She smiles. She looks at ALBUS. She leans down and
gently kisses him on both cheeks.*
She walks away into the woodland. ALBUS stares after her.

SCORPIUS

She didn't kiss me – did you notice? (*He looks at his friend.*)
Are you okay, Albus? You look a little pale. And red. Pale
and red at the same time.

ALBUS

Let's do this.

ACT TWO   SCENE FIVE

THE FORBIDDEN FOREST

The forest seems to grow bigger, thicker, and amongst the trees –
people searching – looking for the missing wizards. But slowly people
melt away until HARRY *is left alone.*

He hears something. He turns to his right.

HARRY
  Albus? Scorpius? Albus?

> *And then he hears the sound of hooves.* HARRY *is startled.*
> *He looks around for where the noise is coming from.*
> *Suddenly* BANE *steps forward into the light. He is a*
> *magnificent centaur.*

BANE
  Harry Potter.

HARRY
  Good. You still recognise me, Bane.

BANE
  You've grown older.

HARRY
  I have.

BANE
  But not wiser. For you trespass on our land.

HARRY

I have always respected the centaurs. We are not enemies.
You fought bravely at the Battle of Hogwarts. And I fought
beside you.

BANE

I did my part. But for my herd, and our honour. Not for you.
And after the battle, the forest was deemed centaur land.
And if you're on our land – without permission – then you
are our enemy.

HARRY

My son is missing, Bane. I need help finding him.

BANE

And he is here? In our forest?

HARRY

Yes.

BANE

Then he is as stupid as you are.

HARRY

Can you help me Bane?

There's a pause. BANE *looks down at* HARRY *imperiously.*

BANE

I can only tell you what I know ... but I tell you not for
your benefit but for the benefit of my herd. The centaurs do
not need another war.

HARRY

Neither do we. What do you know?

BANE

I've seen your son, Harry Potter. Seen him in the
movements of the stars.

HARRY

You've seen him in the stars?

BANE

I can't tell you where he is. I can't tell you how you'll find
him.

HARRY
But you've seen something? You've divined something?

BANE
There is a black cloud around your son, a dangerous black cloud.

HARRY
Around Albus?

BANE
A black cloud that may endanger us all. You'll find your son again, Harry Potter. But then you could lose him forever.

He makes a sound like a horse's cry – and then makes hard away – leaving a bewildered HARRY *behind.*

HARRY *begins to search again – now with even more fervour.*

HARRY
Albus! Albus!

ACT TWO   SCENE SIX

EDGE OF THE FORBIDDEN FOREST

SCORPIUS *and* ALBUS *round a corner to be faced with a gap in the trees . . .*

A gap through which is visible . . . a glorious light . . .

SCORPIUS
And there it is . . .

ALBUS *swallows as he sees it.*

ALBUS
Hogwarts. Never seen this view of it before.

SCORPIUS
Still get a tingle, don't you? When you see it?

And revealed through the trees is HOGWARTS – a splendid mass of bulbous buildings and towers.

From the moment I first heard of it, I was desperate to go. I mean, Dad didn't much like it there but even the way he described it . . . From the age of ten I'd check the *Daily Prophet* first thing every morning – certain some sort of tragedy would have befallen it – certain I wouldn't get to go.

ALBUS
And then you got there and it turned out to be terrible after all.

SCORPIUS
Not for me.

ALBUS *looks at his friend, shocked.*

All I ever wanted to do was go to Hogwarts and have a
mate to get up to mayhem with. Just like Harry Potter. And
I got his son. How crazily fortunate is that.

ALBUS
But I'm nothing like my dad.

SCORPIUS
You're better. You're my best friend, Albus. And this is
mayhem to the nth degree. Which is great, thumbs-up
great, it's just – I have got to say – I don't mind admitting –
I am a tiny bit – just a tiny bit scared.

ALBUS *looks at* SCORPIUS *and smiles.*

ALBUS
You're my best friend too. And don't worry – I have a good
feeling about this.

We hear RON's *voice from off – he's clearly in close
proximity.*

RON
Albus? Albus!

ALBUS *turns towards it, scared.*

ALBUS
But we've got to go – now.

ALBUS *takes the Time-Turner from* SCORPIUS *– he presses
down upon it and the Time-Turner begins to vibrate, and
then explodes into a storm of movement.*
*And with it the stage starts to transform. The two boys
look at it.*

And there is a giant whoosh of light. A smash of noise.
And time stops. And then it turns over, thinks a bit, and
begins spooling backwards, slow at first . . .
And then it speeds up.

ACT TWO   SCENE SEVEN

TRIWIZARD TOURNAMENT, EDGE OF
THE FORBIDDEN FOREST, 1994

Suddenly everything is a riot of noise as a crowd consumes ALBUS
and SCORPIUS.

*And suddenly 'the greatest showman on earth' (his words, not
ours) is on stage, using Sonorus to amplify his voice, and . . . well . . .
he's having a ball.*

LUDO BAGMAN

Ladies and gentlemen, boys and girls, I give you –
the greatest – the fabulous – the one – and the only
TRIWIZARD TOURNAMENT.

There's a loud cheer.

If you're from Hogwarts. Give me a cheer.

There's a loud cheer.

If you're from Durmstrang – give me a cheer.

There's a loud cheer.

AND IF YOU'RE FROM BEAUXBATONS GIVE ME A
CHEER.

There's a slightly limp cheer.

Slightly less enthusiastic from the French there.

SCORPIUS *(smiling)*
This has worked. That's Ludo Bagman.

LUDO BAGMAN
And there they are. Ladies and gentlemen – boys and girls –
I present to you – the reason why we're all here – THE
CHAMPIONS. Representing Durmstrang, what eyebrows,
what a gait, what a boy, there's nothing he won't try on a
broomstick, it's Viktor Krazy Krum.

SCORPIUS *and* ALBUS *(who are really getting into playing the
Durmstrang students now)*
Go go Krazy Krum. Go go Krazy Krum.

LUDO BAGMAN
From the Beauxbatons Academy – zut alors, it's Fleur
Delacour!

There's some polite applause.

And from Hogwarts not one but two students; he makes us
go all weaky at the kneesy, he's Cedric Delicious Diggory.

The crowd go wild.

And then the other – you know him as the Boy Who
Lived, I know him as the boy who keeps surprising us
all . . .

ALBUS
That's my dad.

LUDO BAGMAN
Yes, it's Harry Plucky Potter.

*There's cheering. Particularly from a nervous-looking
girl at the edge of the crowd – this is* YOUNG HERMIONE
(played by the same actress as plays ROSE*). It is noticeable
that the cheering for Harry is slightly less than that for
Cedric.*

And now – silence please all. The – first – task. Retrieving
a golden egg. From a nest of – ladies and gentlemen, boys

and girls, I give you – DRAGONS. And guiding the
dragons – CHARLIE WEASLEY.

There are more cheers.

YOUNG HERMIONE
If you're going to stand so close I'd rather you didn't breathe
on me quite so much.

SCORPIUS
Rose? What are you doing here?

YOUNG HERMIONE
Who's Rose? And what's happened to your accent?

ALBUS *(with a bad accent)*
Sorry. Hermione. He's got you mixed up with someone else.

YOUNG HERMIONE
How do you know my name?

LUDO BAGMAN
And with no time to lose, let's bring out our first
champion – facing a Swedish Short-Snout, I give you –
CEDRIC DIGGORY!

A dragon roar distracts YOUNG HERMIONE, *and* ALBUS
readies his wand.

And Cedric Diggory has entered the stage. And he seems
ready. Scared but ready. He dodges this way. He dodges
that. The girls swoon as he dives for cover. They cry as one:
don't damage our Diggory, Mr Dragon.

SCORPIUS *looks concerned.*

SCORPIUS
Albus, something is going wrong. The Time-Turner, it's
shaking.

*A ticking begins, an incessant, dangerous, ticking. It's
coming from the Time-Turner.*

LUDO BAGMAN

And Cedric skirts left and he dives right – and he readies his wand – what has this young, brave, handsome man got up his sleevies now—

ALBUS (*extending his wand*)

Expelliarmus!

CEDRIC's *wand is summoned to* ALBUS's *hand.*

LUDO BAGMAN

—but no, what's this? Is it Dark Magic or is it something else entirely – Cedric Diggory is disarmed—

SCORPIUS

Albus, I think the Time-Turner – something is wrong . . .

The Time-Turner's ticking gets louder still.

LUDO BAGMAN

It's all going wrong for Diggors. This could be the end of the task for him. The end of the tournament.

SCORPIUS *grabs* ALBUS.

There's a crescendo in the ticking and a flash.

And time is turned back to the present, with ALBUS *hollering in pain.*

SCORPIUS

Albus! Did it hurt you? Albus are you—

ALBUS

What happened?

SCORPIUS

There must be some limit – the Time-Turner must have some kind of *time* limit . . .

ALBUS

Do you think we've done it? Do you think we've changed anything?

Suddenly the stage is invaded from all sides by HARRY, RON (*who now has a side parting and whose wardrobe*

choices have become rather more staid), GINNY *and*
DRACO. SCORPIUS *looks at them all – and slips the Time-*
Turner back into his pocket. ALBUS *looks at them rather*
more blankly – he's in a lot of pain.

RON
I told you. I told you I saw them.

SCORPIUS
I think we're about to find out.

ALBUS
Hello, Dad. Is something wrong?

HARRY *looks at his son disbelievingly.*

HARRY
Yes. You could say that.

ALBUS *collapses on to the floor.* HARRY *and* GINNY *rush to*
help.

ACT TWO   SCENE EIGHT

HOGWARTS, HOSPITAL WING

ALBUS *is asleep in a hospital bed.* HARRY *sits, troubled, beside him. Above them is a picture of a concerned, kindly man. A picture keeping a careful eye on them both.* HARRY *rubs his eyes, stands and walks around the room, stretching his back.*

And then he meets eyes with the painting. Which looks startled to be spotted. And HARRY *looks startled back.*

HARRY

Professor Dumbledore.

DUMBLEDORE

Good evening, Harry.

HARRY

I've missed you. Whenever I've dropped in on the Headmistress lately, your frame's been empty.

DUMBLEDORE

Ah, well, I do like to pop into my other portraits now and then. (*He looks at* ALBUS.) Will he be all right?

HARRY

He's been out twenty-four hours, mostly in order so Madam Pomfrey could reset his arm. She said it was the strangest thing . . . it's like it was broken twenty years ago and allowed to set in the 'most contrary' of directions. She says he'll be fine.

DUMBLEDORE
> A difficult thing, I imagine, to watch your child in pain.

> HARRY *looks up at* DUMBLEDORE, *and then down at* ALBUS.

HARRY
> I've never asked how you felt about me naming him after you, have I?

DUMBLEDORE
> Candidly, Harry, it seemed a great weight to place upon the poor boy.

HARRY
> I need your help. I need your advice. Bane says Albus is in danger. How do I protect my son, Dumbledore?

DUMBLEDORE
> You ask me, of all people, how to protect a boy in terrible danger? We cannot protect the young from harm. Pain must and will come.

HARRY
> So I'm supposed to stand and watch?

DUMBLEDORE
> No. You're supposed to teach him how to meet life.

HARRY
> How? He won't listen.

DUMBLEDORE
> Perhaps he's waiting for you to see him clearly.

> HARRY *frowns as he tries to digest this.*

> (*With sensitivity.*) It is a portrait's curse and blessing to ... hear things. At the school, at the Ministry, I hear people talking ...

HARRY
> And what is the gossip about me and my son?

DUMBLEDORE
> Not gossip. Concern. That you two are struggling. That he's difficult. That he is angry with you. I have formed the impression that – perhaps – you are blinded by your love for him.

HARRY
Blinded?

DUMBLEDORE
You must see him as he is, Harry. You must look for what's wounding him.

HARRY
Haven't I seen him as he is? What's wounding my son? (*He thinks.*) Or is it who's wounding my son?

ALBUS (*mumbles in his sleep*)
Dad . . .

HARRY
This black cloud, it's someone isn't it? Not something?

DUMBLEDORE
Ah really, what does my opinion matter any more? I am paint and memory, Harry, paint and memory. And I never had a son.

HARRY
But I need your advice.

ALBUS
Dad?

> HARRY *looks at* ALBUS *and then back at* DUMBLEDORE. *But* DUMBLEDORE *is gone.*

HARRY
No, where have you gone now?

ALBUS
We're in – the hospital wing?

> HARRY *turns his attention back to* ALBUS.

HARRY (*discombobulated*)
Yes. And you're – you will be fine. For recuperation, Madam Pomfrey wasn't sure what to prescribe and said you should probably eat lots of – chocolate. Actually, do you mind if I have some? I've got something to tell you and I don't think you'll like it.

ALBUS *looks at his dad, what does he have to say? He decides not to engage.*

ALBUS
Okay. I think.

HARRY *takes some chocolate. He eats a big chunk.* ALBUS *looks at his dad, confused.*

Better?

HARRY
Much.

He holds out the chocolate to his son. ALBUS *takes a piece. Father and son munch together.*

The arm, how does it feel?

ALBUS *flexes his arm.*

ALBUS
It feels great.

HARRY *(soft)*
Where did you go Albus? I can't tell you what it did to us – your mum was worried sick . . .

ALBUS *looks up, he is a great liar.*

ALBUS
We decided we didn't want to come to school. We thought we could start again – in the Muggle world – we discovered we were wrong. We were coming back to Hogwarts when you found us.

HARRY
In Durmstrang robes?

ALBUS
The robes were . . . the whole thing – Scorpius and I – we didn't think.

HARRY
And why . . . why did you run? Because of me? Because of what I said?

ALBUS

I don't know. Hogwarts isn't actually that pleasant a place when you don't fit in.

HARRY

And did Scorpius – encourage you to – go?

ALBUS

Scorpius? No.

> HARRY *looks at* ALBUS, *trying to see almost an aura around him, thinking deeply.*

HARRY

I need you to stay away from Scorpius Malfoy.

ALBUS

What? Scorpius?

HARRY

I don't know how you became friends in the first place, but you did – and now – I need you to—

ALBUS

My best friend? My only friend?

HARRY

He's dangerous.

ALBUS

Scorpius? Dangerous? Have you met him? Dad, if you honestly think he's the son of Voldemort—

HARRY

I don't know what he is, I just know you need to stay away from him. Bane told me—

ALBUS

Who's Bane?

HARRY

A centaur with profound divination skills. He said there's a black cloud around you and—

ALBUS

A black cloud?

HARRY
> And I have very good reason to believe that Dark Magic
> is in a resurgence and I need to keep you safe from it. Safe
> from him. Safe from Scorpius.

> ALBUS *hesitates a moment, and then his face strengthens.*

ALBUS
> And if I won't? Stay away from him?

> HARRY *looks at his son, thinking quickly.*

HARRY
> There's a map. It used to be used for those wanting to
> get up to no good. Now we're going to use it to keep an
> eye – a permanent eye – on you. Professor McGonagall
> will watch your every movement. Any time you are seen
> together – she'll come flying – any time you attempt to leave
> Hogwarts – she'll fly. I expect you to go to your lessons, none
> of which you will now share with Scorpius, and between
> times, you will stay in the Gryffindor common room!

ALBUS
> You can't make me go into Gryffindor! I'm Slytherin!

HARRY
> Don't play games Albus, you know what house you are.
> If she finds you with Scorpius – I will fix you with a
> spell – which will allow me eyes and ears into your every
> movement, your every conversation. In the meantime,
> investigations will begin in my department as to his true
> heritage.

ALBUS *(starting to cry)*
> But Dad – you can't – that's just not . . .

HARRY
> I thought for a long time I wasn't a good enough dad for
> you because you didn't like me. It's only now I realise that
> I don't need you to like me, I need you to obey me because
> I'm your dad and I do know better. I'm sorry, Albus. It has
> to be this way.

ACT TWO   SCENE NINE

HOGWARTS, STAIRCASES

ALBUS *pursues* HARRY *across the stage.*

ALBUS
What if I run? I'll run.

HARRY
Albus, get back in bed.

ALBUS
I'll run away again.

HARRY
No. You won't.

ALBUS
I will – and this time I'll make sure Ron can't find us.

RON
Do I hear my name?

> RON *enters on a staircase, his side parting now super-*
> *aggressive, his robes just a little bit too short, his clothes*
> *now spectacularly staid.*

ALBUS
Uncle Ron! Thank Dumbledore. If ever we needed one of
your jokes it's now . . .

> RON *frowns, confused.*

RON

Jokes? I don't know any jokes.

ALBUS

Of course you do. You run a joke shop.

RON *(now supremely confused)*

A joke shop? Well now. Anyway I'm pleased I caught
you ... I was going to bring some sweets – for a, uh, sort of,
a, get well soon, but, uh ... actually Padma – she thinks
about things a lot more – deeply than I do – and she
thought it'd be nicer for you to get something useful for
school. So we got you a – set of quills. Yes. Yes. Yes. Look at
these bad boys. Top of the range.

ALBUS

Who's Padma?

> HARRY *frowns at* ALBUS.

HARRY

Your aunt.

ALBUS

I have an Aunt Padma?

RON

(To HARRY*)* Taken a Confundus Charm to the head, has he?
(To ALBUS*)* My wife, Padma. You remember. Talks slightly
too close to your face, smells a bit minty. *(Leans in.)* Padma,
mother of Panju! *(To* HARRY.*)* That's why I'm here, of course.
Panju. He's in trouble again. I wanted to just send a Howler
but Padma insisted I come in person. I don't know why. He
just laughs at me.

ALBUS

But ... you're married to Hermione.

> *Beat.* RON *doesn't understand this at all.*

RON

Hermione? No. Nooooo. Merlin's beard.

HARRY

Albus has also forgotten that he was sorted into Gryffindor. Conveniently.

RON

Yes, well, sorry, old chap, but you're a Gryffindor.

ALBUS

But how did I get sorted into Gryffindor?

RON

You persuaded the Sorting Hat, don't you remember? Panju bet you that you couldn't get into Gryffindor if your life depended on it, so you chose Gryffindor to spite him. I can't blame you, (*dryly*) we'd all like to wipe the smile off his face sometimes wouldn't we? (*Terrified.*) Please don't tell Padma I said that.

ALBUS

Who's Panju?

> RON *and* HARRY *stare at* ALBUS.

RON

Bloody hell, you're really not yourself are you? Anyway, better go, before I'm sent a Howler myself.

> *He stumbles on, not even an inch of the man he was.*

ALBUS

But that doesn't ... make sense.

HARRY

Albus, whatever you're feigning, it isn't working, I will not change my mind.

ALBUS

Dad, you have two choices, either you take me to—

HARRY

No, you're the one with the choice Albus. You do this, or you get in deeper – much deeper – trouble, do you understand?

> SCORPIUS *appears on the other half of the stairs. He is delighted when he sees* ALBUS.

SCORPIUS

Albus? You're okay. That's fantastic.

HARRY *walks dismissively past* SCORPIUS.

HARRY

He's completely cured. And we've got to go.

ALBUS *looks up at* SCORPIUS *and his heart breaks. He follows his dad – ignoring* SCORPIUS'S *desperate glance as he does.*

SCORPIUS

Are you mad at me? What's going on?

ALBUS *stops and turns to* SCORPIUS.

ALBUS

Did it work? Did any of it work?

SCORPIUS

No ... but, Albus—

HARRY

Albus. Whatever gibberish you're talking, you need to stop it, now. This is your final warning.

ALBUS *looks torn between his dad and his friend.*

ALBUS

I can't, okay?

SCORPIUS

You can't what?

ALBUS

Just – we'll be better off without each other, okay?

SCORPIUS *looks after* ALBUS *as he walks away. Heartbroken.*

ACT TWO   SCENE TEN

HOGWARTS, HEADMISTRESS'S OFFICE

PROFESSOR MCGONAGALL *is full of unhappiness,* HARRY *is full of purpose,* GINNY *is not sure what she's supposed to be.*

PROFESSOR MCGONAGALL
I'm not sure this is what the Marauder's Map was intended for.

HARRY
If you see them together, then get to them as quickly as possible, and keep them separate.

PROFESSOR MCGONAGALL
Harry, are you sure this is the right decision? Because far be it from me to doubt the wisdom of the centaurs but Bane is an extremely angry centaur and . . . it's not beyond him to twist the constellations for his own ends.

HARRY
I trust Bane. Albus is to stay away from Scorpius. For his sake, and others'.

GINNY
I think what Harry means is . . .

HARRY *(with finality)*
The Professor knows what I mean.

> GINNY *looks at* HARRY, *surprised that he'd talk to her that way.*

PROFESSOR MCGONAGALL

Albus has been checked by the greatest witches and wizards in the country and no one can find or sense a hex or a curse.

HARRY

And Dumbledore – Dumbledore said—

PROFESSOR MCGONAGALL

What?

HARRY

His portrait. We spoke. He said some things which made sense—

PROFESSOR MCGONAGALL

Dumbledore is dead, Harry. And I've told you before, portraits don't represent even half of their subjects.

HARRY

He said love had blinded me.

PROFESSOR MCGONAGALL

A headteacher's portrait is a memoir. It is supposed to be a support mechanism for the decisions I have to make. But I was advised as I took this job to not mistake the painting for the person. And you would be well-advised to do the same.

HARRY

But he was right. I see it now.

PROFESSOR MCGONAGALL

Harry, you've been put under enormous pressure, the loss of Albus, the search for him, the fears as to what your scar might mean. But trust me when I tell you, you are making a mistake—

HARRY

Albus didn't like me before. He might not like me again. But he will be safe. With the greatest respect, Minerva – you don't have children—

GINNY

Harry!

HARRY
—you don't understand.

PROFESSOR MCGONAGALL *(deeply hurt)*
I'd hope that a lifetime spent in the teaching profession
would mean—

HARRY
This map will reveal to you where my son is at all times – I
expect you to use it. And if I hear you don't – then I will
come down on this school as hard as I can – using the full
force of the Ministry – is that understood?

PROFESSOR MCGONAGALL *(bewildered by this vitriol)*
Perfectly.

> GINNY *looks at* HARRY, *unsure of what he's become. He
> doesn't look back.*

ACT TWO SCENE ELEVEN

HOGWARTS, DEFENCE AGAINST THE DARK ARTS CLASS

ALBUS *enters the classroom, slightly unsure.*

HERMIONE
 Ah yes. Our train absconder. Finally joining us.

ALBUS
 Hermione?

 He looks amazed. HERMIONE *is standing at the front of
 the lesson.*

HERMIONE
 Professor Granger I believe is my name, Potter.

ALBUS
 What are you doing here?

HERMIONE
 Teaching. For my sins. What are you doing here? Learning
 I hope.

ALBUS
 But you're ... you're ... Minister for Magic.

HERMIONE
 Been having those dreams again have you Potter? Today
 we're going to look at Patronus Charms.

ALBUS *(amazed)*
 You're our Defence Against the Dark Arts teacher?

There are titters.

HERMIONE

Losing patience now. Ten points from Gryffindor for stupidity.

POLLY CHAPMAN (*standing, full of affront*)

No. No. He's doing it deliberately. He hates Gryffindor and everyone knows it.

HERMIONE

Sit down Polly Chapman before this gets even worse. (POLLY *sighs and then sits.*) And I suggest you join her, Albus. And end this charade.

ALBUS

But you're not this mean.

HERMIONE

And that's twenty points from Gryffindor to assure Albus Potter that I am this mean.

YANN FREDERICKS

If you don't sit down right now, Albus . . .

ALBUS *sits.*

ALBUS

Can I just say—

HERMIONE

No, you can't. Just keep quiet Potter, otherwise you'll lose what limited popularity you already have. Now who can tell me what a Patronus is? No? No one. You really are a most disappointing bunch.

HERMIONE *smiles a thin smile. She really is quite mean.*

ALBUS

No. This is stupid. Where's Rose? She'll tell you that you're being ridiculous.

HERMIONE

Who's Rose? Your invisible friend?

ALBUS

Rose Granger-Weasley! Your daughter! (*He realises.*) Of course . . . because you and Ron aren't married Rose—

There's giggling.

HERMIONE

How dare you! Fifty points from Gryffindor. And I assure you if anyone interrupts me again it'll be a hundred points . . .

She stares around the room. No one moves a muscle.

Good. A Patronus is a magical charm, a projection of all your most positive feelings and takes the shape of the animal with whom you share the deepest affinity. It is a gift of light. If you can conjure a Patronus, you can protect yourself against the world. Which, in some of our cases, seems like a necessity sooner rather than later.

———

ACT TWO SCENE TWELVE

HOGWARTS, STAIRCASES

ALBUS *walks up a staircase. Looking around as he does.*

He doesn't see anything. He exits. The staircases move in almost a dance.

SCORPIUS *enters behind him. He thinks he's seen* ALBUS, *he realises he isn't there.*

He slumps down to the floor as the staircase sweeps around.

MADAM HOOCH *enters and walks up the staircase. At the top, she gestures for* SCORPIUS *to move.*

He does. And slopes off – his abject loneliness clear.

ALBUS *enters and walks up one staircase.*

SCORPIUS *enters and walks up another.*

The staircases meet. The two boys look at each other.

Lost and hopeful – all at once.

And then ALBUS *looks away and the moment is broken – and with it, possibly, the friendship.*

And now the staircases part – the two look at each other – one full of guilt – the other full of pain – both full of unhappiness.

ACT TWO SCENE THIRTEEN

HARRY AND GINNY POTTER'S HOUSE, KITCHEN

GINNY *and* HARRY *watch each other warily. There is an argument due, and both of them know it.*

HARRY

This is the right decision.

GINNY

You almost sound convinced.

HARRY

You told me to be honest with him, but actually I needed to be honest with myself, trust what my heart was telling me . . .

GINNY

Harry, you have one of the greatest hearts of any wizard who ever lived, and I do not believe your heart told you to do this.

They hear a knock on the door.

Saved by the door.

She exits.

After a moment, DRACO *enters, consumed by anger but hiding it well.*

131

DRACO

I can't stay long. I won't need long.

HARRY

How can I help?

DRACO

I'm not here to antagonise you. But my son is in tears and I
am his father and so I am here to ask why you would keep
apart two good friends.

HARRY

I'm not keeping them apart.

DRACO

You've changed school timetables, you've threatened both
teachers and Albus himself. Why?

HARRY looks at DRACO carefully and then turns away.

HARRY

I have to protect my son.

DRACO

From Scorpius?

HARRY

Bane told me he sensed a darkness around my son. Near my
son.

DRACO

What are you implying, Potter?

HARRY turns and looks DRACO dead in the eye.

HARRY

Are you sure . . . are you really sure he's yours Draco?

There's a deadly silence.

DRACO

You take that back . . . right now.

*But HARRY doesn't take it back. So DRACO takes his wand
out.*

HARRY
  You do not want to do this.

DRACO
  Yes I do.

HARRY
  I don't want to hurt you, Draco.

DRACO
  How interesting, because I do want to hurt you.

  The two square up. And then release their wands.

DRACO *and* HARRY
  Expelliarmus!

  Their wands repel and then break apart.

DRACO
  Incarcerous!

  HARRY *dodges a blast from* DRACO's *wand.*

HARRY
  Tarantallegra!

  DRACO *throws himself out of the way.*

HARRY
  You've been practising, Draco.

DRACO
  And you've got sloppy, Potter. Densaugeo!

  HARRY *just manages to get out of the way.*

HARRY
  Rictusempra!

  DRACO *uses a chair to block the blast.*

DRACO
  Flipendo!

HARRY is sent twirling through the air. DRACO laughs.

Keep up, old man.

HARRY
We're the same age, Draco.

DRACO
I wear it better.

HARRY
Brachiabindo!

DRACO is bound tightly.

DRACO
That really the best you got? Emancipare!

DRACO releases his own binds.

Levicorpus!

HARRY has to throw himself out of the way.

Mobilicorpus! Oh, this is too much fun . . .

DRACO bounces HARRY up and down on the table. And then as HARRY rolls away, DRACO jumps on to the table – he readies his wand, but as he does HARRY hits him with a spell . . .

HARRY
Obscuro!

DRACO releases himself from his blindfold as soon as it hits.

The two square up – HARRY throws a chair.
DRACO ducks underneath it and slows the chair with his wand.

GINNY
I only left this room three minutes ago!

She looks at the mess of the kitchen. She looks at the chairs suspended in the air. She signals them back to the floor with her wand.

(Drier than dry.) What did I miss?

———

ACT TWO SCENE FOURTEEN

HOGWARTS, STAIRCASES

SCORPIUS *walks unhappily down a staircase.*
   DELPHI *scurries in from the other side.*

DELPHI

So – technically – I shouldn't be here.

SCORPIUS

Delphi?

DELPHI

In fact, technically I'm endangering our entire operation . . .
which is not . . . well, I'm not a natural risk-taker as you
know. I've never been to Hogwarts. Pretty lax security here
isn't there? And so many portraits. And corridors. And
ghosts! This half-headless strange-looking ghost told me
where I could find you, can you believe that?

SCORPIUS

You've never been to Hogwarts?

DELPHI

I was – unwell – as a child – for a few years. Other people
got to go – I did not.

SCORPIUS

You were too – ill? I'm sorry, I didn't know that.

DELPHI

I don't advertise the fact – I prefer not to be seen as a tragic case, you know?

This registers with SCORPIUS. *He looks up to say something but* DELPHI *suddenly ducks from view as a student walks past.* SCORPIUS *tries to look casual until the student passes.*

Have they gone?

SCORPIUS

Delphi, maybe it is too dangerous for you to be here—

DELPHI

Well – someone's got to do something about this.

SCORPIUS

Delphi, none of it worked, time-turning, we failed.

DELPHI

I know. Albus owled me. The history books changed but not enough – Cedric still died. In fact, failing the first task only made him more determined to win the second.

SCORPIUS

And Ron and Hermione have gone completely skewwhiff – and I still haven't figured out why.

DELPHI

And that's why Cedric has to wait. It's all become quite confused and you're entirely right to be keeping hold of the Time-Turner, Scorpius. But what I meant was – someone's got to do something about the two of you.

SCORPIUS

Oh.

DELPHI

You're best friends. Every owl he sends I can feel your absence. He's destroyed by it.

SCORPIUS

Sounds like he's found a shoulder to cry on. How many owls has he sent you now?

DELPHI *smiles softly.*

Sorry. That's – I didn't mean – I just – don't understand what's going on. I've tried to see him, talk to him, but every time I do he runs off.

DELPHI

You know, I didn't have a best friend when I was your age. I wanted one. Desperately. When I was younger I even invented one but—

SCORPIUS

I had one of those too. Called Flurry. We fell out over the correct rules of Gobstones.

DELPHI

Albus needs you, Scorpius. That's a wonderful thing.

SCORPIUS

He needs me to do what?

DELPHI

That's the thing isn't it? About friendships. You don't know what he needs. You only know he needs it. Find him Scorpius. You two – you belong together.

ACT TWO   SCENE FIFTEEN

HARRY AND GINNY POTTER'S HOUSE, KITCHEN

HARRY *and* DRACO *sit far apart.* GINNY *stands between them.*

DRACO
Sorry about your kitchen, Ginny.

GINNY
Oh, it's not my kitchen. Harry does most of the cooking.

There's a silence.

DRACO *(this is hard for him)*
I can't talk to him either. Scorpius. Especially since –
Astoria has gone. I can't even talk about how losing her has
affected him. As hard as I try, I can't reach him. You can't
talk to Albus. I can't talk to Scorpius. That's what this is
about. Not about my son being evil. Because as much as
you might take the word of a haughty centaur, you know
the power of friendship.

HARRY
Draco, whatever you may think—

DRACO
I always envied you them you know – Weasley and Granger.
I had—

GINNY
Crabbe and Goyle.

DRACO
> Two lunks who wouldn't know one end of a broomstick
> from another. You – the three of you – you shone you know?
> You liked each other. You had fun. I envied you those
> friendships more than anything else.

GINNY
> I envied them too.

> HARRY *looks at* GINNY, *surprised.*

HARRY
> I need to protect him—

DRACO
> My father thought he was protecting me. Most of the
> time. People say parenting is the hardest job in the world –
> they're wrong – growing up is. We all just forget how hard it
> was.

> *As hard as he tries to resist them, these words resonate
> with* HARRY.

> I think you have to make a choice – at a certain point –
> of the man you want to be. And I tell you that at that
> time you need a parent or a friend. And if you've learnt
> to hate your parent by then and you have no friends . . .
> then you're all alone. And being alone – that's so hard. I
> was alone. And it sent me to a truly dark place. For a long
> time. Tom Riddle was also a lonely child. You may not
> understand that Harry, but I do – and I think Ginny does
> too.

GINNY
> He's right.

> HARRY *looks up at* GINNY.

DRACO
> Tom Riddle didn't emerge from his dark place. And so Tom
> Riddle became Lord Voldemort. Maybe the black cloud
> Bane saw was Albus's loneliness. His pain. His hatred.

Don't lose the boy. You'll regret it. And so will he. Because he needs you and Scorpius.

HARRY looks at DRACO, he thinks.

He opens his mouth to speak. He thinks.

GINNY
Harry. Will you get the Floo powder or shall I?

ACT TWO SCENE SIXTEEN

HOGWARTS, LIBRARY

SCORPIUS *arrives in the library. He looks left and right. And then he sees* ALBUS. *And* ALBUS *sees him.*

SCORPIUS

Hi.

ALBUS

Scorpius. I can't . . .

SCORPIUS

I know. You're in Gryffindor now. You don't want to see me now. But here I am anyway. Talking to you.

ALBUS

Well, I can't talk, so . . .

SCORPIUS

You have to. You think you can just ignore everything that's happened? The world has gone crazy, have you noticed?

ALBUS

I know, okay? Ron's gone strange. Hermione's a professor, it's all wrong but—

SCORPIUS

And Rose doesn't exist—

ALBUS

I know. Look, I don't understand everything, but you can't
be here.

SCORPIUS

—because of what we did, Rose wasn't even born. Do you
remember being told about the Triwizard Tournament Yule
Ball? All the four Triwizard champions took a partner. Your
dad took Parvati Patil, Viktor Krum took—

ALBUS

Hermione. And Ron got jealous and behaved like a prat.

SCORPIUS

Only he didn't. I found Rita Skeeter's book about them.
And it's very different. Ron took Hermione to the ball.

ALBUS

What?

POLLY CHAPMAN

Ssshhh!

SCORPIUS *looks at* POLLY *and drops his volume.*

SCORPIUS

As friends. And they danced in a friendly way, and it was
nice, and then he danced with Padma Patil and that was
nicer, and they started dating and he changed a bit and
then they got married and meanwhile Hermione became
a—

ALBUS

—psychopath.

SCORPIUS

Hermione was supposed to go to that ball with Krum – do
you know why she didn't? Because she had suspicions the
two strange Durmstrang boys she met before the first task
were somehow involved in the disappearance of Cedric's
wand. She believed we, under Viktor's orders, cost Cedric
the first task . . .

ALBUS

Wow.

SCORPIUS

And without Krum, Ron never got jealous and that jealousy
was all-important and so Ron and Hermione stayed very
good friends but never fell in love – never got married –
never had Rose.

ALBUS *calculates rapidly.*

ALBUS

So that's why Dad's so – did he change too?

SCORPIUS

I'm pretty sure your dad is exactly the same. Head of
Magical Law Enforcement. Married to Ginny. Three kids.

ALBUS

So why is he being such a—

A LIBRARIAN *enters at the back of the room.*

SCORPIUS

Have you heard me, Albus? This is bigger than you and
your dad. Professor Croaker's law – the furthest someone
can go back in time without the possibility of serious harm
to the traveller or time itself is five hours. And we went
back years. The smallest moment, the smallest change, it
creates ripples. And we – we've created really bad ripples.
Rose was never born because of what we did. Rose.

LIBRARIAN

Ssshhh!

ALBUS *thinks quickly.*

ALBUS

Fine, let's go back – fix it. Get Cedric and Rose back.

SCORPIUS

. . . is the wrong answer.

ALBUS

You've still got the Time-Turner, right? No one found it?

SCORPIUS *takes it out of his pocket.*

SCORPIUS

Yes, but . . .

ALBUS *snatches it from his hand.*

No. Don't . . . Albus. Don't you understand how bad things could get?

SCORPIUS *grabs for the Time-Turner,* ALBUS *pushes him back, they wrestle inexpertly.*

ALBUS

Things need fixing, Scorpius. Cedric still needs saving. Rose needs bringing back. We'll be more careful. Whatever Croaker says, trust me, trust us. We'll get it right this time.

SCORPIUS

No. We won't. Give it back, Albus! Give it back!

ALBUS

I can't. This is too important.

SCORPIUS

Yes it's too important – for us. We're not good at this stuff. We'll get it wrong.

ALBUS

Who's saying that we'll get it wrong?

SCORPIUS

I say. Because that's *what we do.* We mess things up. We lose. We're losers, true and total losers. Haven't you realised that yet?

ALBUS *finally gets the upper hand and pins* SCORPIUS *to the ground.*

ALBUS

Well, I wasn't a loser before I met you.

SCORPIUS

Albus, whatever you've got to prove to your dad – this isn't the way—

ALBUS

I don't have anything to prove to my dad. I've got to save Cedric to save Rose. And maybe, without you holding me back, I can make a proper go of it.

SCORPIUS

Without me? Oh poor Albus Potter. With his chip on his shoulder. Poor Albus Potter. So sad.

ALBUS

What are you saying?

SCORPIUS (*exploding*)

Try my life! People look at you because your dad's the famous Harry Potter, saviour of the wizarding world. People look at me because they think my dad is Voldemort. Voldemort.

ALBUS

Don't even—

SCORPIUS

Can you even slightly imagine what that's like? Have you even ever tried? No. Because you can't see beyond the end of your nose. Because you can't see beyond the end of your stupid thing with your dad. He will always be Harry Potter, you know that right? And you will always be his son. And I know it's hard, and the other kids are awful but you have to learn to be okay with that, because – there are worse things, okay?

Beat.

There was a moment I was excited, when I realised time was different, a moment when I thought maybe my mum hadn't got sick. Maybe my mum wasn't dead. But no, turns out, she was. I'm still the child of Voldemort, without a mother, giving sympathy to the boy who doesn't ever give anything back. So I'm sorry if I've ruined your life because I tell you – you wouldn't have a chance of ruining mine – it was already ruined. You just didn't make it better. Because you're a terrible – the most terrible – friend.

ALBUS *digests this. He sees what he's done to his friend.*

PROFESSOR MCGONAGALL (*from off*)
Albus? Albus Potter. Scorpius Malfoy. Are you in there –
together? Because I advise you not to be.

ALBUS *looks at* SCORPIUS, *he pulls a cloak from his bag.*

ALBUS
Quick. We need to hide.

SCORPIUS
What?

ALBUS
Scorpius, look at me.

SCORPIUS
That's the Invisibility Cloak? Isn't it James's?

ALBUS
If she finds us, we'll be forced apart forever. Please. I didn't
understand. Please.

PROFESSOR MCGONAGALL (*from off, trying to give them every
chance*)
I am about to enter.

PROFESSOR MCGONAGALL *comes into the room, the
Marauder's Map in her hands. The boys disappear
beneath the cloak. She looks around exasperated.*

Well, where have they – I never wanted this thing and now
it's playing tricks on me.

*She thinks. She looks back at the map. She identifies
where they should be. She looks around the room.
Objects move as the boys invisibly move past them. She
sees where they're heading, she makes to block them. But
they skirt around her.
A final falling book tells her what they're doing (and
using).*

Your father's cloak.

She looks back at the map, she looks at the boys. She thinks. She smiles to herself.

Well, if I didn't see you, I didn't see you.

She exits. The two boys remove the cloak. They sit in silence for a moment.

ALBUS

Yes, I stole this from James. He's remarkably easy to steal from, his trunk combination is the date he got his first broom. I've found the cloak made avoiding bullies easier.

SCORPIUS nods.

I'm sorry – about your mum. I know we don't talk about her enough – but I hope you know – I'm sorry – it's rubbish – what happened to her – to you.

SCORPIUS

Thanks.

ALBUS

My dad said – said that you were this dark cloud around me. My dad started to think – and I just knew I had to stay away, and if I didn't, Dad said he would—

SCORPIUS

Your dad thinks the rumours are true – I am the son of Voldemort?

ALBUS *(nods)*

His department are currently investigating it.

SCORPIUS

Good. Let them. Sometimes – sometimes I find myself thinking – maybe they're true too.

ALBUS

No. They're not true. And I'll tell you why. Because I don't think Voldemort is capable of having a kind son – and you're kind, Scorpius. To the depths of your belly, to the tips of your fingers. I truly believe Voldemort – Voldemort couldn't have a child like you.

Beat. SCORPIUS *is moved by this.*

SCORPIUS
That's nice – that's a nice thing to say.

ALBUS
And it's something I should have said a long time ago. And
you don't – you couldn't – hold me back – you make me
stronger – and when Dad forced us apart – without you—

SCORPIUS
I didn't much like my life without you in it either.

ALBUS
And I know I'll always be Harry Potter's son – and I will
sort that out in my head – and I know compared to you my
life is pretty good really and that he and I are comparatively
lucky and—

SCORPIUS *(interrupting)*
Albus, as apologies go this is wonderfully fulsome, but
you're starting to talk more about *you* than *me* again, so
probably better to quit while you're ahead.

ALBUS *smiles and stretches out a hand.*

ALBUS
Friends?

SCORPIUS
Always.

SCORPIUS *extends his hand,* ALBUS *pulls* SCORPIUS *up into
a hug.*

That's the second time you've done that.

The two boys break apart and smile.

ALBUS
But I'm pleased we had this argument because it's given me
a really good idea.

SCORPIUS
About what?

ALBUS

It involves the second task. And humiliation.

SCORPIUS

You're still talking about going back in time? Have we been having the same conversation?

ALBUS

You're right – we are losers. We're brilliant at losing and so we should be using our own knowledge here. Our own powers. Losers are taught to be losers. And there's only one way to teach a loser – and we know that better than anyone – humiliation. We need to humiliate him. So in the second task that's what we'll do.

SCORPIUS *thinks – for a long time – and then smiles.*

SCORPIUS

That's a really good strategy.

ALBUS

I know.

SCORPIUS

I mean, quite spectacular. Humiliate Cedric to save Cedric. Clever. And Rose?

ALBUS

That I'm saving as a sparkly surprise. I *can* do it without you – but I *want* you there. Because I want us to do this together. Set things right together. So . . . will you come?

SCORPIUS

But, just a minute, isn't – wasn't – the second task took place in the lake and you're not allowed to leave the school building?

ALBUS *grins.*

ALBUS

Yes. About that . . . we need to find the girls' bathroom on the first floor.

ACT TWO SCENE SEVENTEEN

HOGWARTS, STAIRCASES

RON *is walking down the staircase, consumed, and then he sees* HERMIONE *and his expression changes entirely.*

RON

Professor Granger.

> HERMIONE *looks across, her heart leaps a bit too (though she won't admit it).*

HERMIONE

Ron. What are you doing here?

RON

Panju got in a little trouble in Potions class. Was showing off of course and put the wrong thing with the wrong thing, and now he has no eyebrows and a rather large moustache, apparently. Which doesn't suit him. I didn't want to come but Padma says that when it comes to facial growths, sons need their fathers. Have you done something with your hair?

HERMIONE

Just combed it I suspect.

RON

Well . . . combing it suits you.

> HERMIONE *looks at* RON *slightly strangely.*

HERMIONE
Ron, will you stop looking at me like that?

RON (*summoning confidence*)
You know, Harry's boy Albus – said to me the other day that he thought you and I were – married. Ha ha. Ha. Ha. Ridiculous, I know.

HERMIONE
Very ridiculous.

RON
He even thought we had a daughter. That'd be strange wouldn't it?

The two lock eyes. HERMIONE *is the first to break away.*

HERMIONE
More than strange.

RON
Exactly. We're – friends and that's all.

HERMIONE
Absolutely. Only – friends.

RON
Only – friends. Funny word – friends. Not that funny. Just a word really. Friends. Friend. Funny friend. You, my funny friend, my Hermione. Not that – not *my* Hermione, you understand – not MY Hermione – not MINE – you know, but . . .

HERMIONE
I know.

There's a pause. Neither of them moves the smallest inch. Everything feels too important for movement. Then RON *coughs.*

RON
Well. Must get on. Sort Panju out. Teach him the finer arts of moustache grooming.

He walks on, he turns, looks at HERMIONE. *She looks back, he hurries on again.*

Your hair really does very much suit you.

ACT TWO   SCENE EIGHTEEN

HOGWARTS, HEADMISTRESS'S OFFICE

PROFESSOR MCGONAGALL *is onstage on her own. She looks at the map. She frowns to herself. She taps it with her wand. She smiles to herself at a good decision made.*

PROFESSOR MCGONAGALL
Mischief managed.

There's a rattling.

The whole stage seems to vibrate.

GINNY *is the first through the fireplace, and then* HARRY.

GINNY
Professor, I can't say that ever gets more dignified.

PROFESSOR MCGONAGALL
Potter. You're back. And you seem to have finally ruined my carpet.

HARRY
I need to find my son. We need to.

PROFESSOR MCGONAGALL
Harry, I've considered this and decided I want no part of it. Whatever you threaten, I—

HARRY
Minerva, I come here in peace, not war. I should never have spoken to you that way.

PROFESSOR MCGONAGALL
I just don't think I can interfere in friendships and I believe—

HARRY
I need to say sorry to you and sorry to Albus, will you give me that chance?

DRACO *arrives behind them with a bang of soot.*

PROFESSOR MCGONAGALL
Draco?

DRACO
He needs to see his son, and I need to see mine.

HARRY
Like I say – peace – not war.

PROFESSOR MCGONAGALL *studies his face, she sees the sincerity she needs to see. She takes the map back out of her pocket. She opens it up.*

PROFESSOR MCGONAGALL
Well, peace is certainly something I can be part of.

She taps it with her wand. Sighs.

I solemnly swear that I'm up to no good.

The map is lit into action.

Well, they are together.

DRACO
In the girls' bathroom on the first floor. What on earth would they be doing there?

ACT TWO   SCENE NINETEEN

HOGWARTS, GIRLS' BATHROOM

SCORPIUS *and* ALBUS *enter a bathroom. In the centre of it is a large Victorian sink.*

SCORPIUS

So let me get this right – the plan is Engorgement . . .

ALBUS

Yes. Scorpius, that soap if you may . . .

SCORPIUS *fishes a soap out of the sink.*

Engorgio!

He fires a bolt from his wand across the room. The soap blows up to four times its size.

SCORPIUS

Nice. Consider me engorgimpressed.

ALBUS

The second task was the lake task. They had to retrieve something which was stolen from them, which turned out to be—

SCORPIUS

—people they loved.

ALBUS

Cedric used a Bubble-Head Charm to swim through the
lake. All we do is follow him in there, and use Engorgement
to turn him into something rather larger. We know the
Time-Turner doesn't give us long, so we're going to be
quick. Get to him and Engorgio his head and watch him
float out of the lake – away from the task – away from the
competition . . .

SCORPIUS

But – you still haven't told me how we're going to actually
get to the lake . . .

*And then suddenly a jet of water emerges from the sink
and after it ascends a very wet* MOANING MYRTLE.

MOANING MYRTLE

Whoah. That feels good. Never used to enjoy that. But
when you get to my age, you take what you can . . .

SCORPIUS

Of course – you're a genius – Moaning Myrtle . . .

MOANING MYRTLE *swoops down on to* SCORPIUS.

MOANING MYRTLE

What did you call me? Do I moan? Am I moaning now? *Am
I? Am I?*

SCORPIUS

No.

MOANING MYRTLE

What's my name?

SCORPIUS

Myrtle.

MOANING MYRTLE

Exactly – Myrtle. Myrtle Elizabeth Warren – a pretty
name – my name. No need for the Moaning.

She giggles.

It's been a while. Boys. In my bathroom. In my girls'
bathroom. Well, that's not right . . . but then again, I always

did have a soft spot for the Potters. And I was moderately partial to a Malfoy too. Now how can I help you pair?

ALBUS

You were there Myrtle – in the lake. They wrote about you. There must be a way out of these pipes.

MOANING MYRTLE

I've been everywhere. But where specifically were you thinking?

ALBUS

The second task. The lake task. In the Triwizard Tournament. Twenty-five years ago. Harry and Cedric.

MOANING MYRTLE

Such a shame the pretty one had to die. Not that your father is not pretty – but Cedric Diggory – you'd be amazed at how many girls I had to hear doing love incantations in this very bathroom . . . and the weeping after he was taken.

ALBUS

Help us Myrtle, help us get into that same lake.

MOANING MYRTLE

You think I can help you travel in time?

ALBUS

We need you to keep a secret.

MOANING MYRTLE

I love secrets. I won't tell a soul. Cross my heart and hope to die. Or – the equivalent. For ghosts. You know.

ALBUS *nods at* SCORPIUS, *who reveals the Time-Turner.*

ALBUS

We can travel in time. You're going to help us travel the pipes. We're going to save Cedric Diggory.

MOANING MYRTLE *(grins)*

Well, that sounds like fun.

ALBUS

And we've no time to lose.

MOANING MYRTLE

This very sink. This very sink empties directly into the lake. It breaks every bylaw but this school has always been antiquated. Dive in and you will be piped straight to it.

ALBUS pulls himself into the sink, dumping his cloak as he does. SCORPIUS copies.

ALBUS hands SCORPIUS some green foliage in a bag.

ALBUS

Some for me and some for you.

SCORPIUS

Gillyweed? We're using Gillyweed? To breathe under water?

ALBUS

Just like my dad did. Now, are you ready?

SCORPIUS

Remember, this time, we can't be caught out by the clock . . .

ALBUS

Five minutes, that's all we allow for, before we get pulled back to the present.

SCORPIUS

Tell me this is all going to be okay.

ALBUS *(grinning)*

It's all going to be entirely okay. Are you ready?

ALBUS takes the Gillyweed and disappears down.

SCORPIUS

No, Albus – Albus –

He looks up, he and MOANING MYRTLE are alone.

MOANING MYRTLE

I do like brave boys.

SCORPIUS *(a little bit scared, a tiny bit brave)*

Then I'm entirely ready. For whatever comes.

He takes the Gillyweed and disappears down.

MOANING MYRTLE *is left alone onstage.*

*There is a giant whoosh of light and smash of noise.
And time stops. And then it turns over, thinks a bit, and
begins spooling backwards . . .*

The boys are gone.

HARRY *appears at a run, a deep frown on his face, behind
him* DRACO, GINNY *and* PROFESSOR MCGONAGALL.

HARRY

Albus . . . Albus . . .

GINNY

He's gone.

They find the boys' cloaks on the ground.

PROFESSOR MCGONAGALL *(consulting the map)*

He's disappeared. No, he's travelling under Hogwarts
grounds, no, he's disappeared—

DRACO

How is he doing this?

MOANING MYRTLE

He's using a rather pretty trinket thingy.

HARRY

Myrtle!

MOANING MYRTLE

Oops, you caught me. And I was trying so hard to hide.
Hello, Harry. Hello, Draco. Have you been bad boys again?

HARRY

What trinket is he using?

MOANING MYRTLE

I think it was a secret, but I could never keep anything
from you Harry. How is it you've grown handsomer and
handsomer as you've aged?

HARRY

My son is in danger. I need your help. What are they doing
Myrtle?

MOANING MYRTLE

He's after saving a dishy boy. A certain Cedric Diggory.

HARRY *immediately realises what's happened, and is horrified.*

PROFESSOR MCGONAGALL

But Cedric Diggory died years ago . . .

MOANING MYRTLE

He seemed quite confident he could get around that fact. He's very confident Harry, just like you.

HARRY

He heard me talking – to Amos Diggory . . . could he have . . . the Ministry's Time-Turner. No, that's impossible.

PROFESSOR MCGONAGALL

The Ministry has a Time-Turner? I thought they were destroyed?

MOANING MYRTLE

Isn't everyone so naughty?

DRACO

Can someone please explain what's going on?

HARRY

Albus and Scorpius are not disappearing and reappearing – they're travelling. Travelling in time.

ACT TWO   SCENE TWENTY

TRIWIZARD TOURNAMENT, LAKE, 1995

LUDO BAGMAN

Ladies and gentlemen, boys and girls, I give you –
the greatest – the fabulous – the one – and the only
TRIWIZARD TOURNAMENT! If you're from Hogwarts.
Give me a cheer.

There's a loud cheer.

And now ALBUS *and* SCORPIUS *are swimming through
the lake. Descending through the water with graceful
ease.*

If you're from Durmstrang – give me a cheer.

There's a loud cheer.

AND IF YOU'RE FROM BEAUXBATONS GIVE ME A
CHEER.

There's a slightly less limp cheer.

The French are getting into this.

And they're off . . . Viktor's a shark, of course he is, Fleur
looks remarkable, ever plucky Harry is using Gillyweed,
clever Harry, very clever – and Cedric – well, Cedric, what
a treat ladies and gentlemen, Cedric is using a Bubble

Charm to cruise through the lake.

> CEDRIC DIGGORY *approaches them through the water,*
> *a bubble over his head.* ALBUS *and* SCORPIUS *raise their*
> *wands together and fire an Engorgement Charm through*
> *the water.*
> *He turns and looks at them confused. And it hits him.*
> *And around him the water glows gold.*
> *And then* CEDRIC *starts to grow – and grow again – and*
> *grow some more.*
> *He looks around himself – entirely panicked. And the boys*
> *watch as* CEDRIC *ascends helplessly through the water.*

But no, what's this . . . Cedric Diggory is ascending out of
the water and seemingly out of the competition. Oh, ladies
and gentlemen, we don't have our winner but we certainly
have our loser. Cedric Diggory is turning into a balloon
and this balloon wants to fly. Fly, ladies and gentlemen,
fly. Fly out of the task and out of the tournament and – oh
my, it gets wilder still, around Cedric fireworks *explode*
declaiming – 'Ron loves Hermione' – and the crowd love
that – oh, ladies and gentlemen, the look on Cedric's face.
It's quite some picture, it's quite some sight, it's quite some
tragedy. This is a humiliation, there's no other word for it.

> *And* ALBUS *smiles widely and high-fives* SCORPIUS *in the*
> *water.*
> *And* ALBUS *points up, and* SCORPIUS *nods, and they start*
> *to swim ever upward. And as* CEDRIC *ascends people start*
> *to laugh, and everything changes.*
> *The world becomes darker. The world becomes almost*
> *black in fact.*
> *And there's a flash. And a bang. And the Time-Turner*
> *ticks to a stop. And we're back in the present.*
> SCORPIUS *suddenly emerges, shooting up through the*
> *water. And he's triumphant.*

SCORPIUS
Woooo – hoooooo!

He looks around, surprised. Where's Albus? He puts his arms into the air.

We did it!

He waits another beat.

Albus?

Albus still doesn't emerge. SCORPIUS *treads water, he thinks and then he ducks back into the water.*
He emerges back up again. Now thoroughly panicked. He looks around.

Albus ... ALBUS ... ALBUS.

And there's a whisper in Parseltongue. Which travels fast around the audience. He's coming. He's coming. He's coming.

DOLORES UMBRIDGE
Scorpius Malfoy. Get out of the lake. Get out of the lake. Right now.

She pulls him out of the water.

SCORPIUS
Miss. I need help. Please, Miss.

DOLORES UMBRIDGE
Miss? I'm Professor Umbridge, the Headmistress of your school, I'm no Miss.

SCORPIUS
You're the Headmistress? But I ...

DOLORES UMBRIDGE
I am the Headmistress and however important your family may be – it doesn't give you an excuse to dilly-dally, to mess about.

SCORPIUS

There's a boy in this lake. You need to get help. I'm looking for my friend, Miss. Professor. Headmaster. One of Hogwarts's students, Miss. I'm looking for Albus Potter.

DOLORES UMBRIDGE

Potter? Albus Potter? There's no such student. In fact, there hasn't been a Potter at Hogwarts for years – and that boy didn't turn out so well. Not so much rest in peace, Harry Potter, more rest in perpetual despair. Total troublemaker.

SCORPIUS

Harry Potter's dead?

Suddenly from around the auditorium, the feel of a breath of the wind. Some black robes arise around people. Black robes that become black shapes. That become Dementors.

Flying Dementors through the auditorium. These black deadly shapes, these black deadly forces. They are everything to be feared. And they suck the spirit from the room.

The wind continues. This is Hell. And then right from the back of the room and whispering around everyone. Words said with an unmistakeable voice. The voice of

VOLDEMORT . . .

Haaarry Potttttter . . .

Harry's dream has come to life.

DOLORES UMBRIDGE

Have you swallowed something funny in there? Become a Mudblood without any of us noticing? Harry Potter died over twenty years ago as part of that failed coup on the school – he was one of those Dumbledore terrorists we bravely overthrew at the Battle of Hogwarts. Now come along – I don't know what game you're playing but you're upsetting the Dementors and entirely ruining Voldemort Day.

And the Parseltongue whispers grow louder and louder.
Grow monstrously loud. And giant banners with snake
symbols upon them descend over the stage.

And SCORPIUS is at the horrified heart of it all.

SCORPIUS
Voldemort Day?

We cut to black.

END OF PART ONE

PART TWO

PART TWO

ACT THREE

ACT THREE SCENE ONE

HOGWARTS, HEADMISTRESS'S OFFICE

And now we're firmly in a reworked world.

And it is a world of darkness.

There is a coating of ash over the Earth – which gives it a pallor of uncertainty and dread.

This is reflected in the staging – in the music – but above all else in the tone of the choices we make.

HARRY is dead. VOLDEMORT lives and rules. Nothing is as it should be.

SCORPIUS enters the office of DOLORES UMBRIDGE. He is dressed in darker, blacker robes. He has a pensive look on his face. He is aware of danger from all sides and remains coiled and alert throughout.

DOLORES UMBRIDGE
Scorpius. Thank you so much for coming to see me.

SCORPIUS
Headmistress.

DOLORES UMBRIDGE
Scorpius, I've thought for a long time that you have Head Boy potential, as you know. Pure-blooded, a natural leader, wonderfully athletic . . .

SCORPIUS
Athletic?

DOLORES UMBRIDGE

No need to be modest, Scorpius. I've seen you on the
Quidditch pitch, there's rarely a Snitch you don't catch.
You are a highly valued student. Valued by the faculty.
Valued especially by me. I've positively glowed about you
in dispatches to the Augurey. Our work together, flushing
out the more dilettante students has made this school a
safer – purer – place.

SCORPIUS

Has it?

There is the sound of a scream from off. SCORPIUS *turns
towards it. But he dismisses the thought. He must and he
will control himself.*

DOLORES UMBRIDGE

But in the three days since I found you in that lake on
Voldemort Day, you've become . . . odder and odder – in
particular, this sudden obsession with Harry Potter . . .

SCORPIUS

I don't . . .

DOLORES UMBRIDGE

Questioning everyone you can about the Battle of
Hogwarts. How Potter died. Why Potter died. And this
ludicrous fascination with Cedric Diggory. Scorpius – we've
checked you for hexes and curses – there were none we can
see – so I'm asking if there's anything I can do – to restore
you to what you were . . .

SCORPIUS

No. No. Consider me restored. Temporary aberration.
That's all.

DOLORES UMBRIDGE

So we can continue our work together?

SCORPIUS

We can.

> *She puts her hand to her heart, and touches her wrists together.*

DOLORES UMBRIDGE
For Voldemort and Valour.

SCORPIUS (*trying to copy*)
For – um – yes.

ACT THREE SCENE TWO

HOGWARTS, GROUNDS

And now the stage begins to spin and SCORPIUS *spins with it, looking for something – anything – to answer the mess he's in.*

    KARL *and* YANN *are full of vim and vigour. They approach* SCORPIUS *hard.*

KARL JENKINS
Hey Scorpion King.

    SCORPIUS *is high-fived. It's painful, he takes it.*

YANN FREDERICKS
We're still on right, tomorrow night?

KARL JENKINS
Because we are ready to spill some proper Mudblood guts.

    They exit.

POLLY CHAPMAN
Scorpius.

    POLLY CHAPMAN *is standing on the stairs,* SCORPIUS *whirls towards her.*

SCORPIUS
Polly Chapman?

POLLY CHAPMAN

Shall we cut to it? I know everyone is waiting to know who
you're going to ask because, you know, you need to ask
someone and I've been asked by three people already and I
know I'm not alone in refusing them all. In case, you know,
you were to ask me.

SCORPIUS

Right.

POLLY CHAPMAN

Which would be great. If you were interested. Which
rumour is – you are. And I just want to make clear – at
this moment – that I am also interested. And that isn't a
rumour. That's a – f-a-c-t – fact.

SCORPIUS

That's um – great, but – what are we talking about?

POLLY CHAPMAN

The Blood Ball of course – who you – the Scorpion King,
are taking to the Blood Ball.

SCORPIUS

You – Polly Chapman – want me to take you to a – ball?

There is the sound of screaming behind him.

What is that screaming?

POLLY CHAPMAN

Mudbloods of course. In the dungeons. Your idea wasn't it?
What's going on with you? Oh Potter, I've got blood on my
shoes again . . .

She bends and carefully cleans the blood off her shoes.

Like the Augurey insists – the future is ours to make – so
here I am – making a future – with you. For Voldemort and
Valour.

SCORPIUS

For Voldemort it is.

POLLY *walks on,* SCORPIUS *looks agonised after her. What is this world – and what is he within it?*

He rotates on and into . . .

ACT THREE   SCENE THREE

MINISTRY OF MAGIC, OFFICE OF THE HEAD OF MAGICAL LAW ENFORCEMENT

DRACO *is impressive in a way we haven't seen. He has the smell of power about him and he wears the authority well. Flying down either side of the room are Augurey flags – with the bird emblazoned in a fascistic manner.*

DRACO
You are late.

SCORPIUS
This is your office?

DRACO
You are late and unapologetic. Maybe you are determined to compound the problem.

SCORPIUS
You're Head of Magical Law Enforcement?

DRACO
How dare you! How dare you embarrass me and keep me waiting and then not apologise for it!

SCORPIUS
Sorry.

DRACO
Sir.

SCORPIUS *looks up, trying to work out what's going on with his dad.*

SCORPIUS
Sorry, sir.

DRACO
I did not bring you up to be sloppy, Scorpius. I did not bring you up to humiliate me at Hogwarts.

SCORPIUS
Humiliate you, sir?

DRACO
Harry Potter, asking questions about Harry Potter, of all the embarrassing things. How dare you disgrace the Malfoy name.

A dark thought flashes through SCORPIUS's *head.*

SCORPIUS
Oh no. Are you responsible? No. No. You can't be.

DRACO
Scorpius . . .

SCORPIUS
The *Daily Prophet* today – three wizards blowing up bridges to see how many Muggles they can kill with one blast – is that you?

DRACO
Be very careful.

SCORPIUS *advances towards his dad, accusing him at every step.*

SCORPIUS
The 'Mudblood' death camps, the torture, the burning alive of those that oppose him. How much of that is you? Mum always told me that you were a better man than I could see, but this is what you really are isn't it? A murderer, a torturer, a—

DRACO *rises up and pulls* SCORPIUS *hard on to the table.*

The violence is surprising and deadly.

DRACO

Do not use her name in vain, Scorpius. Do not score points that way. She deserves better than that.

SCORPIUS *says nothing. Horrified and scared.* DRACO *reads this. He lets go of* SCORPIUS's *head. He doesn't like hurting his son.*

And no, those idiots blasting Muggles, that's not my doing, though it'll be me the Augurey asks to bribe the Muggle Prime Minister with gold . . . Did your mother really say that of me?

SCORPIUS

She said that grandfather didn't like her very much – opposed the match – thought she was too Muggle-loving – too weak – but that you defied him for her. She said it was the bravest thing she'd ever seen.

DRACO

She made being brave very easy, your mother.

SCORPIUS

But that was – another you.

He looks at his dad, who looks back with a frown.

I've done bad things, you've done worse. What have we become, Dad?

DRACO

We haven't become anything – we simply are as we are.

SCORPIUS

The Malfoys. The family you can always rely on to make the world a murkier place.

This hits home with DRACO, *he looks carefully at* SCORPIUS.

DRACO

This business at the school – what's inspired it?

SCORPIUS
I don't want to be who I am.

DRACO
And what's brought that on?

SCORPIUS *desperately thinks for a way of describing his story.*

SCORPIUS
I've seen myself in a different way.

DRACO
You know what I loved most about your mother? She could always help me find light in the darkness. She made the world – my world anyway – less – what was the word you used – 'murky'.

SCORPIUS
Did she?

DRACO *studies his son.*

DRACO
There's more of her in there than I thought.

Beat. He looks at SCORPIUS *carefully.*

Whatever you're doing – do it safely. I can't lose you too.

SCORPIUS
Yes. Sir.

DRACO *looks at his son one last time – trying to understand his head.*
He moves his hand over his wrists in the now-familiar way.

DRACO
For Voldemort and Valour.

SCORPIUS *looks at him and backs out of the room.*

SCORPIUS
For Voldemort and Valour.

ACT THREE   SCENE FOUR

HOGWARTS, LIBRARY

SCORPIUS *enters the library and starts to desperately look through books. He finds a history book.*

SCORPIUS
How did Cedric become a Death Eater? What have I missed? Find me some – light in the darkness.

CRAIG BOWKER JR
Why are you here?

SCORPIUS *turns to look at a rather desperate-looking* CRAIG.

SCORPIUS
Why can't I be here?

CRAIG BOWKER JR
It's not ready yet. I'm working as fast as I can. But Professor Snape sets so much of it, and writing the essay in two different ways. I mean, I'm not complaining . . . sorry.

SCORPIUS
Start again. From the beginning. What's not ready?

CRAIG BOWKER JR
Your Potions homework. And I'm happy to do it – grateful even – and I know you hate homework and books, and I never let you down, you know that.

SCORPIUS
I – hate – homework?

CRAIG BOWKER JR
You're the Scorpion King. Of course you hate homework.
What are you doing with *A History of Magic*? I could do
that assignment too?

Pause. SCORPIUS *looks at* CRAIG *a moment and then
throws him the history book.* CRAIG *exits, clutching it.*
After a moment SCORPIUS *frowns as a thought occurs.*

SCORPIUS
Did he say Snape?

ACT THREE   SCENE FIVE

HOGWARTS, POTIONS CLASSROOM

SCORPIUS *runs into the Potions classroom. Slamming back the door.*
SEVERUS SNAPE *looks up at him.*

SNAPE
Did no one teach you to knock, boy?

>SCORPIUS *looks up at* SNAPE, *slightly breathless, slightly unsure, slightly exultant.*

SCORPIUS
Severus Snape. This is an honour.

SNAPE
Professor Snape will do fine. You may behave like a king at this school Malfoy, but that doesn't make us all your subjects.

SCORPIUS
But you're the answer . . .

>SNAPE *remains as caustic as he's ever been.*

SNAPE
How very pleasant for me. If you've got something to say boy, then please say it . . . if not, close the door on your way out.

SCORPIUS

I need your help.

SNAPE

I exist to serve.

SCORPIUS

I just don't know what help I – need. Are you still undercover now? Are you still working secretly for Dumbledore?

SNAPE

Dumbledore? Dumbledore's dead. And my work for him was public – I taught in his school.

SCORPIUS

No. That's not all you did. You watched the Death Eaters for him. You advised him. Everyone thought you'd murdered him – but it turned out you'd been supporting him. You saved the world.

SNAPE snarls with fear and fury.

SNAPE

These are very dangerous allegations, boy. And don't think the Malfoy name will prevent me inflicting punishment.

SCORPIUS

What if I was to tell you there was another world – another world in which Voldemort was defeated at the Battle of Hogwarts, in which Harry Potter and Dumbledore's Army won, how would you feel then ...

SNAPE

I'd say that the rumours of Hogwarts's beloved Scorpion King losing his mind are well founded.

SCORPIUS

There was a stolen Time-Turner. I stole a Time-Turner. With Albus. We tried to bring Cedric Diggory back from the dead, when he was dead. We tried to stop him winning the Triwizard Tournament. But by doing so we turned him into an almost different person entirely.

SNAPE

Harry Potter won that Triwizard Tournament.

SCORPIUS

He wasn't supposed to do it alone. Cedric was supposed to win it with him. But we humiliated him out of the tournament. And as a result of that humiliation he became a Death Eater. I can't work out what he did in the Battle of Hogwarts – whether he killed someone or – but he did something and it changed everything.

SNAPE

Cedric Diggory killed only one wizard and not a significant one – Neville Longbottom.

SCORPIUS

Oh, of course, that's it! Professor Longbottom was supposed to kill Nagini, Voldemort's snake. Nagini had to die before Voldemort could die. That's it! You've solved it! We destroyed Cedric, he killed Neville, Voldemort won the battle. Can you see? Can you see it?

SNAPE

I can see this is a Malfoy game. Get out before I alert your father and plunge you into deep trouble.

SCORPIUS *thinks and then plays his final, desperate, card.*

SCORPIUS

You loved his mother. I don't remember everything. I know you loved his mother. Harry's mother. Lily. I know you spent years undercover. I know without you the war could never have been won. How would I know this if I hadn't seen the other world . . . ?

SNAPE *says nothing, overwhelmed.*

Only Dumbledore knew, am I right? And when you lost him you must have felt so alone. I know you're a good man. Harry Potter told his son you're a great man.

SNAPE *looks at* SCORPIUS, *unsure what's going on. Is this a trick? He is quite seriously at a loss.*

SNAPE
Harry Potter is dead.

SCORPIUS
Not in my world. He said you were the bravest man he'd ever met. He knew, you see – he knew your secret – what you did for Dumbledore. And he admired you for it – greatly. And that's why he named his son – my best friend – after you both. Albus Severus Potter.

SNAPE *is stopped. He is deeply moved.*

Please – for Lily, for the world, help me.

SNAPE *thinks and then walks up to* SCORPIUS, *taking out his wand as he does.* SCORPIUS *steps back, scared.* SNAPE *fires his wand at the door.*

SNAPE
Colloportus!

An invisible lock slams into place. SNAPE *opens a hatch at the back of the classroom.*

Well, come on then . . .

SCORPIUS
Just a question, but where – exactly – are we going?

SNAPE
We've had to move many times. Everywhere we've settled they destroyed. This will take us to a room hidden in the roots of the Whomping Willow.

SCORPIUS
Okay, who's we?

SNAPE
Oh. You'll see.

ACT THREE SCENE SIX

CAMPAIGN ROOM

The underground. An atmosphere of earth, dust and hopeless (but necessary) endeavour.

SCORPIUS *is pinned to the table by a rather magnificent-looking* HERMIONE. *Her clothes may be faded but her eyes blaze, she is full warrior now and it rather suits her.*

HERMIONE
You make one more move and your brain will be a frog and your arms will be rubber.

SNAPE *enters the room after* SCORPIUS.

SNAPE
Safe. He's safe. (*Beat.*) You know you never could listen. You were a terrible bore of a student and you're a terrible bore of – whatever you are.

HERMIONE
I was an excellent student.

SNAPE
You were moderate to average. He's on our side!

SCORPIUS
I am, Hermione.

HERMIONE *looks at* SCORPIUS, *still very distrustful.*

187

HERMIONE

Most people know me as Granger. And I don't believe a word you say, Malfoy.

SCORPIUS

It's all my fault. My fault. And Albus's.

HERMIONE

Albus? Albus Dumbledore? What's Albus Dumbledore got to do with this?

SNAPE

He doesn't mean Dumbledore. You may need to sit down.

> RON *runs in. His hair spiked. His clothes scruffy. He is less good at the rebel look than* HERMIONE *is.*

RON

Snape, a royal visit and – (*he sees* SCORPIUS, *and is immediately alarmed*) what's he doing here?

> *He fumbles out his wand.*

I'm armed and – entirely dangerous and seriously advise you—

> *He realises his wand is around the wrong way and turns it right.*

—to be very careful—

SNAPE

He's safe, Ron.

> RON *looks at* HERMIONE, *who nods.*

RON

Thank Dumbledore for that.

ACT THREE SCENE SEVEN

CAMPAIGN ROOM

HERMIONE *is sitting studying the Time-Turner as* RON *tries to digest it all.*

RON

>So you're telling me that the whole of history rests on . . .
>Neville Longbottom? This is pretty wild.

HERMIONE

>It's true, Ron.

RON

>Right. And you're sure because . . .

HERMIONE

>What he knows about Snape – about all of us – there's no
>way he could . . .

RON

>Maybe he's a really good guesser?

SCORPIUS

>I'm not. Can you help?

RON

>We're the only ones that can. Dumbledore's Army has
>shrunk considerably since its peak, in fact—

>*He takes a moment, this is painful for him.*

>—we're pretty much all that's left, but we've kept fighting

on. Hiding in plain sight. Doing our best to tickle their nose hairs. Granger here is a wanted woman. I'm a wanted man.

SNAPE (*dryly*)
Less-wanted.

HERMIONE
To be clear: in this other world . . . before you meddled?

SCORPIUS
Voldemort is dead. Killed in the Battle of Hogwarts. Harry is Head of Magical Law Enforcement. You're Minister for Magic.

> HERMIONE *stops, surprised by this, she looks up with a smile.*

HERMIONE
I'm Minister for Magic?

RON (*wanting to join the fun*)
Brilliant. What do I do?

SCORPIUS
You run Weasleys' Wizard Wheezes.

> RON's *face drops.*

RON
Okay, so, she's Minister for Magic and I run a – joke shop?

> SCORPIUS *looks at* RON's *hurt face.*

SCORPIUS
You're mostly focused on bringing up your kids.

RON
Great. I expect their mother is hot.

SCORPIUS (*blushing*)
Well . . . um . . . depends what you think of . . . the thing is, you two, sort of have kids – together. A daughter and a son.

> *The two look up, astonished.*

Married. In love. Everything. You were shocked the other

time too. When you were Defence Against the Dark Arts teacher and Ron was married to Padma. You're *constantly* surprised by it.

> HERMIONE *and* RON *both look at each other and then look away. And then* RON *looks back.* RON *clears his throat repeatedly. With less conviction each time.*

HERMIONE
Close your mouth when you're looking at me, Weasley.

> RON *does so. Though he remains discombobulated.*

And – Snape? What does Snape do in this other world?

SNAPE
I'm dead, presumably.

> *He looks at* SCORPIUS, *who tries desperately to mask the truth, but can't help himself reflecting it.* SNAPE *smiles thinly.*

You were a little too surprised to see me. How?

SCORPIUS
Bravely.

SNAPE
Who?

SCORPIUS
Voldemort.

SNAPE
How very irritating.

> *There's a silence as* SNAPE *digests this.*

Still, there's glory in being taken down by the Dark Lord himself, I suppose.

HERMIONE
I'm sorry, Severus.

> SNAPE *looks at her, and then swallows the pain. He indicates* RON *with a flick of his head.*

SNAPE
Well, at least I'm not married to him.

HERMIONE
Which spells did you use?

SCORPIUS
Expelliarmus in the first task and Engorgio in the second.

RON
Simple Shield Charms should set both of those right.

SNAPE
And then you left?

SCORPIUS
The Time-Turner took us back, yes. That's the thing – this Time-Turner, you only get five minutes in the past.

HERMIONE
And can you still only move in time not space?

SCORPIUS
Yes, yes, it's – uh – you travel back in the same spot you stand in—

HERMIONE
Interesting.

SNAPE *and* HERMIONE *both know what this means.*

SNAPE
Then it's just me and the boy.

HERMIONE
No offence, Snape, but I'm not trusting this to anyone ... it's too important.

SNAPE
Hermione, you're the most wanted rebel in the wizarding world. Doing this will require you to go outside. When was the last time you were outside?

HERMIONE
Not for a long time but—

SNAPE
> If you're found outside, the Dementors will kiss you – they'll
> suck out your soul . . .

HERMIONE
> Severus, I'm done with living off scraps, making failed
> attempts at coups, this is our chance to reset the world.

She nods at RON, *who pulls down a map.*

> The first task of the tournament took place at the edge
> of the Forbidden Forest. We turn time here, get to the
> tournament – block the spell and then return safely. With
> precision – it can be done and it won't require us to show
> our faces outside in our time at all. Then we'll turn time
> again, make our way to the lake, and reverse the second
> task.

SNAPE
> You're risking everything—

HERMIONE
> We get this right, Harry's alive, Voldemort's dead and the
> Augurey is gone. For that no risk is too great. Though I am
> sorry what it will cost you.

SNAPE
> Sometimes costs are made to be borne.

The two look at each other, SNAPE *nods,* HERMIONE *nods
back,* SNAPE's *face crumbles slightly.*

> I didn't just quote Dumbledore, did I?

HERMIONE (*with a smile*)
> No, I'm pretty sure that's pure Severus Snape.

She turns to SCORPIUS, *she indicates the Time-Turner.*

> Malfoy.

SCORPIUS *brings her the Time-Turner. She smiles at it,
excited to use a Time-Turner again, excited to use it for
this.*

Let's hope this works.

She takes the Time-Turner, it begins to vibrate, and then it explodes into a storm of movement.

And there is a giant whoosh of light. A smash of noise.

And time stops. And then it turns over, thinks a bit, and begins spooling backwards, slow at first . . .

There is a bang and a flash, and our gang disappears.

ACT THREE   SCENE EIGHT

EDGE OF THE FORBIDDEN FOREST, 1994

And we watch our scene from Part One replayed, but at the back of the stage rather than the front. We pick out ALBUS *and* SCORPIUS *in their Durmstrang robes. And through it all we hear the 'brilliant' (his words again)* LUDO BAGMAN.

   SCORPIUS, HERMIONE, RON *and* SNAPE *watch on anxiously.*

LUDO BAGMAN
   And Cedric Diggory has entered the stage. And he seems ready. Scared but ready. He dodges this way. He dodges that. The girls swoon as he dives for cover. They cry as one: don't damage our Diggory, Mr Dragon. And Cedric skirts left and he dives right – and he readies his wand—

SNAPE
   This is taking too long. The Time-Turner is spinning.

LUDO BAGMAN
   What has this young, brave, handsome man got up his sleevies now?

   As ALBUS *attempts to summon Cedric's wand,* HERMIONE *blocks his spell. He looks at his wand, disconsolate, unsure why it hasn't worked.*

And then the Time-Turner spins and they look at it and panic as they're pulled into it.

A dog – he's transfigured a stone into a dog – dog diggity Cedric Diggory – you are a doggy dynamo.

ACT THREE   SCENE NINE

EDGE OF THE FORBIDDEN FOREST

They are returned from time, at the edge of the forest, and RON *is in a lot of pain.* SNAPE *looks around, immediately aware of the mess they're in.*

RON
  Ow. Ow. Owwwwwww.

HERMIONE
  Ron ... Ron ... what has it done to you?

SNAPE
  Oh no, I knew it.

SCORPIUS
  The Time-Turner did something to Albus too. The first time we went back.

RON
  Useful – time to – ow – tell us.

SNAPE
  We're above ground. We need to move. Now.

HERMIONE
  Ron, you can still walk, come on ...

  RON *does stand up, shouting in pain.* SNAPE *raises his wand.*

SCORPIUS
Did it work?

HERMIONE
We blocked the spell. Cedric kept his wand. Yes. It worked.

SNAPE
But we came back to the wrong place – we are outside. You are outside.

RON
We need to use the Time-Turner again – get out of here—

SNAPE
We need to find shelter. We're horribly exposed.

Suddenly from around the auditorium, the feel of the breath of an icy wind.

Some black robes arise around people. Black robes that become black shapes. That become Dementors.

HERMIONE
Too late.

SNAPE
This is a disaster.

HERMIONE *(she realises what she has to do)*
They're after me, not any of you.

Ron. I love you and I always have. But the three of you need to run. Go. Now.

RON
What?

SCORPIUS
What?

RON
Can we talk about the love thing first?

HERMIONE
This is still Voldemort's world. And I am done with it. Reversing the next task will change everything.

SCORPIUS
But they'll kiss you. They'll suck out your soul.

HERMIONE

And then you'll change the past. And then they won't. Go. Now.

The Dementors sense them. From all sides screaming shapes descend.

SNAPE

Go! We go.

He pulls on SCORPIUS's *arm.* SCORPIUS *reluctantly goes with him.*

HERMIONE *looks at* RON, *who hasn't moved.*

HERMIONE

You're supposed to be going, too.

RON

Well, they are after me a bit and I really am in quite a lot of pain. And, you know, I'd rather be here. Expecto—

As he reaches up to cast the spell, HERMIONE *stops his arm.*

HERMIONE

Let's keep them here and give the boy the best chance we can.

RON *looks at her and then nods sadly.*

HERMIONE

A daughter and a son.

He smiles gently at her; their love is true and total.

RON

And a son. I liked that idea too.

He looks around – he knows his fate.

I'm scared.

HERMIONE

Kiss me.

RON *thinks and then does. And the Dementors descend and the two are yanked apart. They're pinned to the ground and then pulled into the air. We watch as a golden-whitish haze is pulled from their bodies. They have their souls sucked from them. And it is terrifying.*

SCORPIUS *and* SNAPE *re-enter at the back of the stage, aware of what's already been lost.*

SNAPE
Let's get down to the water. Walk. Don't run.

SNAPE *looks at* SCORPIUS.

Stay calm, Scorpius. They may be blind but they can sense your fear.

SCORPIUS
They just sucked out their souls.

A Dementor swoops down low over them and settles in front of SCORPIUS.

SNAPE
Think of something else, Scorpius. Occupy your thoughts.

But SCORPIUS *can't occupy his thoughts.*

SCORPIUS
I feel cold. I can't see. There's a fog inside me – around me.

SNAPE
You're a king, and I'm a professor. They'll only attack with good reason. Think about those you love, think about why you're doing this.

SCORPIUS *(utterly consumed)*
I can hear my mother. She wants me – my – help but she knows I can't – help.

SNAPE
Listen to me, Scorpius. Think about Albus. You're giving up your kingdom for Albus, right?

SCORPIUS *is helpless. Consumed by all the Dementor is making him feel. And* SNAPE *knows he needs to open his heart to save him.*

SNAPE

One person. All it takes is one person. I couldn't save Harry for Lily. So now I give my allegiance to the cause she believed in. And it's possible – that along the way I started believing in it myself.

SCORPIUS *steps decisively away from the Dementor.*

SCORPIUS

The world changes and we change with it. I am better off in this world. But the world is not better. And I don't want that.

Suddenly DOLORES UMBRIDGE *emerges behind them.*

DOLORES UMBRIDGE

Professor Snape!

SNAPE

Professor Umbridge.

DOLORES UMBRIDGE

Have you heard the news? We've caught that traitorous Mudblood Hermione Granger. She was just out here.

SNAPE

That's – fantastic.

DOLORES *is staring at* SNAPE. *He looks back.*

DOLORES UMBRIDGE

With you. Granger was with you.

SNAPE

With me? You're mistaken.

DOLORES UMBRIDGE

With you and Scorpius Malfoy. A student I'm becoming increasingly concerned about.

SCORPIUS

Well . . .

PART TWO

SNAPE

Dolores, we're late for class, so if you'll excuse us . . .

DOLORES UMBRIDGE

If you're late for class, why are you not heading back to the school? Why are you heading to the lake?

There's a moment of pure silence. And then SNAPE *does something hugely unusual – he smiles.*

SNAPE

How long have you suspected?

DOLORES UMBRIDGE *rises off the ground. She opens her arms wide, full of Dark Magic. She takes out her wand.*

DOLORES UMBRIDGE

Years. And I should have acted upon it far earlier.

SNAPE *is faster with his wand.*

SNAPE

Depulso!

DOLORES *is propelled backwards through the air.*

She always was too grand for her own good. There's no turning back now.

The sky turns even blacker still around them.

Expecto Patronum!

SNAPE *sends forward a Patronus, and it's a beautiful white shape of a doe.*

SCORPIUS

A doe? Lily's Patronus.

SNAPE

Strange isn't it? What comes from within.

Dementors start to appear all around them. SNAPE *knows what this means.*

You need to run. I will keep them at bay for as long as I can.

SCORPIUS
Thank you for being my light in the darkness.

SNAPE looks at him, every inch a hero, he softly smiles.

SNAPE
Tell Albus – tell Albus Severus – I'm proud he carries my name. Now go. Go!

The doe looks at SNAPE – who nods at it – and then back at SCORPIUS, and then it starts to run.

SCORPIUS thinks and then runs after the doe and around him the world gets scarier. A blood-curdling scream goes up at one side. He sees the lake and throws himself inside.

SNAPE readies himself.

The Dementors descend and SNAPE is pulled hard to the ground and then pushed high into the air as his soul is ripped from him. The screams seem to multiply.

The doe turns to him, with beautiful eyes and disappears.

There is a bang and a flash. And then silence. And then there's more silence.

It's so still, it's so peaceful, it's so perfectly tranquil.

And then SCORPIUS ascends to the surface. Breathing deeply. He looks around himself. Breathing deep, panicked breaths. He looks up at the sky. The sky certainly seems – bluer than before.

There is a moment of pure calm.

And then ALBUS ascends after SCORPIUS. There's a silence. SCORPIUS just looks at ALBUS, disbelieving. Both boys breathe in and out.

ALBUS
Whoah!

An impenetrable smile grows across SCORPIUS's face.

SCORPIUS

Albus!

ALBUS

That was close! Did you see that Merman? The guy with the – and then the thing with the – whoah!

SCORPIUS

It's you!

ALBUS

It was weird though – I thought I saw Cedric start to expand – but then he sort of started shrinking again – and I looked at you and you had your wand out . . .

SCORPIUS

You have no idea how good it is to see you again.

ALBUS

You just saw me two minutes ago.

SCORPIUS hugs ALBUS in the water, a difficult task.

SCORPIUS

A lot has happened since then.

ALBUS

Careful. You're drowning me. What are you wearing?

SCORPIUS

What am I wearing? (*He pulls off his cloak.*) What are you wearing? Yes! You're in Slytherin.

ALBUS

Did it work? Did we do anything?

SCORPIUS

No. And it's brilliant.

ALBUS looks at him – disbelieving.

ALBUS

What? We failed.

SCORPIUS

Yes. YES. AND IT'S AMAZING.

He splashes hard in the water. ALBUS *pulls himself out to the bank.*

ALBUS
Scorpius. Have you been eating too many sweets again?

SCORPIUS
There you go you see – all dry humour and Albus-y. I love it!

ALBUS
Now I'm starting to get worried . . .

HARRY *enters and sprints to the side of the water. Followed quickly by* DRACO, GINNY *and* PROFESSOR MCGONAGALL.

HARRY
Albus. Albus. Are you okay?

SCORPIUS *(overjoyed)*
Harry! It's Harry Potter! And Ginny. And Professor McGonagall. And Dad. My dad. Hi. Dad.

DRACO
Hello, Scorpius.

ALBUS
You're all here.

GINNY
And Myrtle told us everything.

ALBUS
What is going on?

PROFESSOR MCGONAGALL
You're the one who's just returned from time. Why don't you tell us?

SCORPIUS *immediately registers what they know.*

SCORPIUS
Oh no. Oh bother. Where is it?

ALBUS
Just returned from where?

SCORPIUS
I've lost it! I've lost the Time-Turner.

ALBUS (*looking at* SCORPIUS, *deeply annoyed*)
You've lost what?

HARRY
Time to cut the pretence, Albus.

PROFESSOR MCGONAGALL
I think you've got some explaining to do.

ACT THREE   SCENE TEN

HOGWARTS, HEADMISTRESS'S OFFICE

DRACO, GINNY *and* HARRY *stand behind a contrite-looking* SCORPIUS *and* ALBUS. PROFESSOR MCGONAGALL *is fuming.*

PROFESSOR MCGONAGALL
So to be clear – you illegally jumped off the Hogwarts Express, you invaded and stole from the Ministry of Magic, you took it upon yourself to change time, whereupon you disappeared two people—

ALBUS
I agree it doesn't sound good.

PROFESSOR MCGONAGALL
And your response to disappearing Hugo and Rose Granger-Weasley was to go back in time again – and this time – instead of losing two people you lost a huge number of people and killed your father – and in doing so you resurrected the worst wizard the world has ever known and heralded in a new age of Dark Magic. (*Dry.*) You're correct, Mr Potter, it doesn't sound good does it? Are you aware how stupid you've been?

SCORPIUS
Yes, Professor.

ALBUS *hesitates a moment. He looks at* HARRY.

ALBUS
Yes.

HARRY
Professor, if I may—

PROFESSOR MCGONAGALL (*sharp*)
You may not. What you choose to do as parents is your matter, but this is my school, and these are my students, and I will choose what punishment they will face.

DRACO
Seems fair.

HARRY *looks at* GINNY, *who shakes her head.*

PROFESSOR MCGONAGALL
I should expel you but (*with a look to* HARRY) all things considered – I think it might be safer for you to remain in my care. You are in detention for – well, you can consider yourself in detention for the rest of the year. Christmas is cancelled for you. You can forget visiting Hogsmeade ever again. And that's just the start . . .

Suddenly HERMIONE *bursts in. All action and resolve.*

HERMIONE
What did I miss?

PROFESSOR MCGONAGALL (*fierce*)
It is considered polite to knock when entering a room, Hermione Granger, maybe you missed that.

HERMIONE (*realises she's over-stepped*)
Ah.

PROFESSOR MCGONAGALL
If I could also give a detention to you, Minister, I would. Keeping hold of a Time-Turner, of all the stupid things!

HERMIONE
In my defence—

PROFESSOR MCGONAGALL
And in a *bookcase*. You kept it in a bookcase! It's almost laughable.

HERMIONE
Minerva. (*There is an intake of breath;* HERMIONE *realises her mistake.*) Professor McGonagall—

PROFESSOR MCGONAGALL
Your children didn't exist!

HERMIONE *has no reply to that.*

This happened in my school, under my watch. After all that Dumbledore did, I couldn't live with myself . . .

HERMIONE
I know.

PROFESSOR MCGONAGALL *composes herself for a moment. She turns firmly to the boys.*

PROFESSOR MCGONAGALL (*to* ALBUS *and* SCORPIUS)
Your intentions to save Cedric were honourable if misguided. And it does sound as if you were brave, Scorpius, and you, Albus, but the lesson even your father sometimes failed to heed is that bravery doesn't forgive stupidity. Always think. Think what's possible. A world controlled by Voldemort is—

SCORPIUS
A horrific world.

PROFESSOR MCGONAGALL
You are so young. (*She looks at* HARRY, DRACO, GINNY *and* HERMIONE.) You're all so young. You have no idea how dark the wizarding wars got. You were – reckless – with the world some people – some very dear friends of mine and yours – sacrificed a huge amount to create and sustain.

ALBUS
Yes, Professor.

SCORPIUS
Yes, Professor.

PROFESSOR MCGONAGALL
Go on. Get out. The lot of you. And find me that Time-Turner.

ACT THREE SCENE ELEVEN

HOGWARTS, SLYTHERIN DORMITORY

ALBUS *is sitting in his room.* HARRY *enters and looks at his son, full of anger, but cautious to not let it spill.*

HARRY
Thanks for letting me come up.

ALBUS *turns, he nods at his dad. He's being cautious too.*

No luck, as yet, with the Time-Turner searching. They're negotiating with the Merpeople to dredge the lake.

He sits down, uncomfortably.

This is a nice room.

ALBUS
Green is a soothing colour isn't it? I mean Gryffindor rooms are all well and good, but the trouble with red is – it is said to send you a little mad – not that I'm casting aspersions . . .

HARRY
Can you explain why you tried to do this?

ALBUS
I thought I could – change things – I thought Cedric – it's unfair.

HARRY
Of course it's unfair Albus, don't you think I know that?

I was there. I saw him die. But to do this . . . to risk all
this . . .

ALBUS
I know.

HARRY (*failing to contain his anger*)
If you were trying to do as I did, you went the wrong way
about it. I didn't volunteer for adventure, I was forced
into it. You did something really reckless – something
really stupid and dangerous – something that could have
destroyed everything—

ALBUS
I know. Okay, I know.

> *Pause.* ALBUS *wipes away a tear,* HARRY *notices it and
> takes a breath. He pulls himself back from the brink.*

HARRY
I was wrong too – to think Scorpius was Voldemort's son.
He wasn't a black cloud.

ALBUS
No.

HARRY
And I've locked away the map. You won't see it again. Your
mum left your room exactly as it was when you ran away –
you know that? Wouldn't let me go in – wouldn't let anyone
go in – you really scared her . . . and me.

ALBUS
Really scared you?

HARRY
Yes.

ALBUS
I thought Harry Potter wasn't afraid of anything?

HARRY
Is that how I make you feel?

> ALBUS *looks at his dad, trying to figure him out.*

ALBUS

I don't think Scorpius said, but when we returned after
failing to fix the first task, I was suddenly in Gryffindor
house, nothing was better between us then either – so the
fact that I'm in Slytherin – that's not the reason for our
problems. It's not just about that.

HARRY

No. I know. It's not just about that.

HARRY *looks at* ALBUS.

Are you okay, Albus?

ALBUS

No.

HARRY

No. Nor me.

ACT THREE   SCENE TWELVE

DREAM, GODRIC'S HOLLOW, GRAVEYARD

YOUNG HARRY *stands looking at a gravestone covered in bunches of flowers. He has a small bunch of flowers in his hand.*

AUNT PETUNIA
Go on then, lay down your grotty little flowers and then let's go. I already hate this poxy little village, I don't know why I even had the thought – Godric's Hollow, Godless Hollow more like, the place is clearly a hive of filth – go on, chop chop.

> YOUNG HARRY *approaches the grave. He stands a moment more.*

Now, Harry ... I don't have time for this. Duddy has his Cubs tonight and you know he hates to be late.

YOUNG HARRY
Aunt Petunia. We're their last living relatives, right?

AUNT PETUNIA
Yes. You and I. Yes.

YOUNG HARRY
And – they weren't popular? You said they didn't have any friends?

AUNT PETUNIA
Lily tried – bless her – she tried – it wasn't her fault, but she

213

repelled people – by her very nature. It was her intensity, it was her – manner, it was her – way. And your father – obnoxious man – extraordinarily obnoxious. No friends. Neither of them.

YOUNG HARRY

So my question is – why are there so many flowers? Why are there flowers all over their grave?

> AUNT PETUNIA *looks around, she sees all the flowers as if for the first time and it moves her hugely. She approaches and then sits by her sister's grave, trying hard to fight the emotions as they come to her but succumbing all the same.*

AUNT PETUNIA

Oh. Yes. Well, I suppose there are a – few. Must have blown over from the other graves. Or someone's playing a trick. Yes, I think that's most likely, some young rapscallion with too much time on his hands, has gone around collecting flowers from all the other graves and deposited them here—

YOUNG HARRY

But they're all marked with their names ... Lily and James, what you did, we will never forget ... Lily and James, your sacrifice—

VOLDEMORT

I smell guilt, there is a stench of guilt upon the air.

AUNT PETUNIA (*to* YOUNG HARRY)

Get away. Get away from there.

> *She pulls him back.* VOLDEMORT'*s hand rises into the air above the Potters' gravestone, the rest of him rises after. We don't see his face but his body provides a jagged, horrific shape.*

I knew it. This place is dangerous. The sooner we leave Godric's Hollow the better.

YOUNG HARRY *is pulled from the stage, but turns to face*
VOLDEMORT.

VOLDEMORT
Do you still see with my eyes, Harry Potter?

YOUNG HARRY *exits disturbed as* ALBUS *bursts from within*
VOLDEMORT's *cloak. He reaches out a desperate hand*
towards his dad.

ALBUS
Dad ... Dad ...

There's some words spoken in Parseltongue.
He's coming. He's coming. He's coming.
And then a scream.
And then right from the back of the room and whispering
around everyone. Words said with an unmistakeable
voice. The voice of VOLDEMORT ...
Haaarry Pottttter ...

ACT THREE SCENE THIRTEEN

HARRY AND GINNY POTTER'S HOUSE, KITCHEN

HARRY *is in a horrible state. Petrified by what he thinks his dreams are telling him.*

GINNY
Harry? Harry? What is it? You were screaming . . .

HARRY
They haven't stopped. The dreams.

GINNY
They weren't likely to stop immediately. It's been a stressful time and—

HARRY
But I was never in Godric's Hollow with Petunia. This doesn't—

GINNY
Harry, you're really scaring me.

HARRY
He's still here, Ginny.

GINNY
Who's still here?

HARRY
Voldemort. I saw Voldemort and Albus.

GINNY
And Albus . . . ?

HARRY

    He said – Voldemort said – 'I smell guilt, there is a stench of guilt upon the air.' He was talking to me.

    HARRY *looks at her. He touches his scar. Her face falls.*

GINNY

    Harry, is Albus still in danger?

    HARRY's *face grows white.*

HARRY

    I think we all are.

ACT THREE   SCENE FOURTEEN

HOGWARTS, SLYTHERIN DORMITORY

The two boys are supposed to be asleep, but SCORPIUS *can't sleep.*
He gets out of bed and leans ominously over ALBUS's *bedhead.*

SCORPIUS
Albus ... Psst ... Albus.

But ALBUS *doesn't wake, so* SCORPIUS *goes nuclear.*

ALBUS!

ALBUS *wakes with a shock.* SCORPIUS *laughs.*

ALBUS
Pleasant. That's a pleasant and not scary way to wake
up.

SCORPIUS
You know it's the strangest of things but ever since being
in the scariest place imaginable I'm pretty much good with
fear. I am – Scorpius the Dreadless. I am – Malfoy the
Unanxious.

ALBUS
Good.

SCORPIUS
I mean, normally, being in lockdown, being in constant
detention. It'd break me but now – what's the worst they

can do? Bring back Mouldy Voldy and have him torture me?
Nope.

ALBUS

You're scary when you're in a good mood, you know that?

SCORPIUS

When Rose came up to me today in Potions and called
me Bread Head, I almost hugged her. No, there's no almost
about it, I actually tried to hug her, and then she kicked me
in the shin.

ALBUS

I'm not sure being fearless is going to be good for your
health.

> SCORPIUS *looks at* ALBUS; *his face grows more*
> *contemplative.*

SCORPIUS

You don't know how good it is to be back here, Albus. I
hated it there.

ALBUS

Apart from the Polly Chapman fancying you bits.

SCORPIUS

Cedric was a different person entirely – dark, dangerous.
My dad – doing anything they wanted him to. And me?
I discovered another Scorpius you know? Entitled, angry,
mean – people were frightened of me. It feels like we were
all tested and we all – failed.

ALBUS

But you changed things. You had a chance and you
changed time back. Changed yourself back.

SCORPIUS

Only because I knew what I should be.

> ALBUS *digests this.*

ALBUS

Do you think I've been tested too? I have, haven't I?

SCORPIUS

No. Not yet.

ALBUS

You're wrong. The stupid thing wasn't going back once –
anyone can make that mistake – the stupid thing was being
arrogant enough to go back twice.

SCORPIUS

We both went back, Albus.

ALBUS

And why was I so determined to do this? Cedric? Really?
No. I had something to prove. My dad's right – he didn't
volunteer for adventure – me, this, it's all my fault – and if it
wasn't for you everything could have gone Dark.

SCORPIUS

But it didn't. And you're to thank for that as much as me.
When the Dementors were – inside my head – Severus
Snape told me to think of you. You may not have been
there Albus, but you were fighting – fighting alongside me.

ALBUS *nods. Touched by this.*

And saving Cedric – that wasn't such a bad idea – not
in my head anyway – though, you know right – that we
definitely can't try again.

ALBUS

Yes. I do. I do know that.

SCORPIUS

Good. Then you can help me destroy this.

SCORPIUS *pulls the Time-Turner from under his pillow
and reveals it to an astonished* ALBUS.

ALBUS

I'm pretty sure you told everyone that was on the bottom of
a lake.

SCORPIUS

Turns out Malfoy the Unanxious is a pretty good liar.

ALBUS
  Scorpius, we should tell someone about this . . .

SCORPIUS
  Who? The Ministry kept it before, do you really trust them
  not to keep it again? Only you and I have experienced how
  dangerous this is, that means you and I have to destroy it.
  No one can do what we did Albus. No one. No, (*grandly*)
  it's time that time-turning became a thing of the past.

ALBUS (*smiling at his friend*)
  You're quite proud of that phrase, aren't you?

SCORPIUS (*grinning back*)
  Been working on it all day.

ACT THREE   SCENE FIFTEEN

HOGWARTS, SLYTHERIN DORMITORY

HARRY *and* GINNY *move quickly through the dormitory.* CRAIG BOWKER JR *trails after them.*

CRAIG BOWKER JR
    Can I repeat again? This is against the rules and it's the middle of the night.

HARRY
    I need to find my son.

CRAIG BOWKER JR
    I know who you are, Mr Potter, but even you must understand that it's against school covenant for parents or professors to enter a house quarters without express permission from . . .

    PROFESSOR MCGONAGALL *charges in behind them.*

PROFESSOR MCGONAGALL
    Please don't be tiresome, Craig.

HARRY
    You got our message? Good.

CRAIG BOWKER JR *(shocked)*
    Headmistress. I'm – I was just—

    HARRY *pulls open a bed curtain.*

PROFESSOR MCGONAGALL
He's gone?

HARRY
Yes.

PROFESSOR MCGONAGALL
And young Malfoy?

GINNY *pulls open another.*

GINNY
Oh no.

PROFESSOR MCGONAGALL
Then let's turn this school upside down. Craig, we've work to do . . .

GINNY *and* HARRY *stay looking at the bed.*

GINNY
Haven't we been here before?

HARRY
Something feels even worse this time.

GINNY *looks at her husband, full of fear.*

GINNY
You spoke to him earlier?

HARRY
Yes.

GINNY
You came to his dorm and talked to him?

HARRY
You know I did.

GINNY
What did you say to our son, Harry?

HARRY *can hear the accusation in her voice.*

HARRY
I tried to be honest like you said – I didn't say anything.

GINNY

And you controlled yourself? How heated did it get?

HARRY

. . . I don't think I . . . you think I've scared him away again?

GINNY

I can forgive you for one mistake Harry, maybe even two, but the more mistakes you make, the harder to forgive you it becomes.

ACT THREE   SCENE SIXTEEN

HOGWARTS, OWLERY

SCORPIUS and ALBUS emerge on to a roof bathed in silver light. There's soft hooting all around them.

SCORPIUS
So, I think a simple Confringo.

ALBUS
Definitely not. For something like this you need Expulso.

SCORPIUS
Expulso? Expulso and we'll be clearing bits of Time-Turner from this owlery for days.

ALBUS
Bombarda?

SCORPIUS
And wake up everyone in Hogwarts? Maybe Stupefy. They were originally destroyed using Stupefy . . .

ALBUS
Exactly, it's been done before – let's do something new, something fun.

SCORPIUS
Fun? Look, many wizards overlook the importance of choosing the right spell but this really matters. I think it's a much-underestimated part of modern witchcraft.

DELPHI

'A much-underestimated part of modern witchcraft' – you
two are the greatest, you know that?

SCORPIUS *looks up, surprised to see* DELPHI *has emerged
behind them.*

SCORPIUS

Wow. You're . . . um . . . what are you doing here?

ALBUS

It felt important to send an owl – let her know what we're
doing – you know?

SCORPIUS *looks at his friend accusingly.*

This concerns her too.

SCORPIUS *thinks, and then nods, accepting this.*

DELPHI

What concerns me? What's this about?

ALBUS *gets out the Time-Turner.*

ALBUS

We need to destroy the Time-Turner. The things Scorpius
saw after the second task . . . I'm so sorry. We can't risk
going back again. We can't save your cousin.

DELPHI *looks at it and then at them both.*

DELPHI

Your owl said so little . . .

ALBUS

Imagine the worst possible world, and then double it.
People being tortured – Dementors everywhere – a despotic
Voldemort – my dad dead, me never born, the world
surrounded by Dark Magic. We just – we can't allow that to
happen.

DELPHI *hesitates. And then her face breaks.*

DELPHI
Voldemort ruled? He was alive?

SCORPIUS
He ruled everything. It was terrible.

DELPHI
Because of what we did?

SCORPIUS
Humiliating Cedric turned him into a very angry young
man and then he became a Death Eater and – and – it all
went wrong. Really wrong.

DELPHI looks at SCORPIUS's face carefully. Her face sinks.

DELPHI
A Death Eater?

SCORPIUS
And a murderer. He killed Professor Longbottom.

DELPHI
Then – of course – we need to destroy it.

ALBUS
You understand?

DELPHI
I'll go further than that – I'll say Cedric would have
understood. We'll destroy it together, and then we'll go to
my uncle. Explain the situation.

ALBUS
Thank you.

*DELPHI smiles at them sadly, and then takes the Time-
Turner. She looks at it and her expression changes
slightly.*

Oh, nice mark.

DELPHI
What?

*DELPHI's cloak has loosened. An Augurey tattoo is visible
on the back of her neck.*

ALBUS

> On your back. I hadn't noticed it before. The wings. Is that what the Muggles call a tattoo?

DELPHI

> Oh. Yes. Well, it's an Augurey.

SCORPIUS

> An Augurey?

DELPHI

> Haven't you met them in Care of Magical Creatures? They're sinister-looking black birds that cry when rain's coming. Wizards used to believe that the Augurey's cry foretold death. When I was growing up, my guardian kept one in a cage.

SCORPIUS

> Your ... guardian?

> > DELPHI *looks at* SCORPIUS. *Now she has the Time-Turner she's enjoying this game.*

DELPHI

> She used to say it was crying because it could see I was going to come to a sticky end. She didn't like me much. Euphemia Rowle ... she only took me in for the gold.

ALBUS

> Why would you want a tattoo of her bird, then?

DELPHI

> It reminds me that the future is mine to make.

ALBUS

> Cool. I might get an Augurey tattoo.

SCORPIUS

> The Rowles were pretty extreme Death Eaters.

> *A thousand thoughts whir inside* SCORPIUS's *head.*

ALBUS

> Come on, let's get destroying ... Confringo? Stupefy? Bombarda? Which would you use?

SCORPIUS
Give it back. Give us back the Time-Turner.

DELPHI
What?

ALBUS
Scorpius? What are you doing?

SCORPIUS
I don't believe you ever were ill. Why didn't you come to Hogwarts? Why are you here now?

DELPHI
I'm trying to bring my cousin back!

SCORPIUS
They called you the Augurey. In – the other world – they called you the Augurey.

A slow smile grows on DELPHI's *face.*

DELPHI
The Augurey? I rather like that.

ALBUS
Delphi?

She's too quick. Levelling her wand, she repels SCORPIUS. *And she is far stronger –* SCORPIUS *tries to keep her back, but she quickly overpowers him.*

DELPHI
Fulgari!

SCORPIUS's *arms are bound in vicious, luminous cords.*

SCORPIUS
Albus. Run.

ALBUS *looks around, bewildered. And then starts to run.*

DELPHI
Fulgari!

ALBUS *is propelled to the floor, his hands tied by the same brutal binding.*

And that is the first spell I've had to use on you. I thought I'd have to use plenty more. But you're far easier to control than Amos – children, particularly male children, are so naturally pliant aren't they? Now, let's sort this mess out once and for all . . .

ALBUS

But why? But what? But who are you?

DELPHI

Albus. I am the new past.

She pulls ALBUS*'s wand from him and snaps it.*

I am the new future.

She pulls SCORPIUS*'s wand from him and snaps it.*

I am the answer this world has been looking for.

ACT THREE   SCENE SEVENTEEN

MINISTRY OF MAGIC, HERMIONE'S OFFICE

RON *is sitting on* HERMIONE's *desk as she studies some files.*

RON

I can't get over it really. The fact that in some realities we aren't even, you know, married.

HERMIONE

Ron whatever this is – I've got ten minutes until the goblins show up to talk security at Gringotts—

RON

I mean, we've been together so long – and married for so long – I mean, *so* long—

HERMIONE

If this is your way of saying you want a marital break Ron, then, to be clear, I will skewer you with this quill.

RON

Shut up. Will you shut up for once? I want to do one of those marriage renewal things I've read about. Marriage renewal. What do you think?

HERMIONE *(melting)*

You want to marry me again?

RON

Well, we were only young when we did it the first time and I got very drunk and – well, to be honest, I can't

remember much of it and . . . the truth is – I bloody love
you Hermione Granger – and whatever time says – I'd like
the opportunity to say so in front of lots of other people.
Again. Sober.

She looks at him, she smiles, she pulls him to her, she
kisses him.

HERMIONE
You're sweet.

RON
And you taste of toffee.

HERMIONE *laughs.* HARRY, GINNY *and* DRACO *walk in on*
them as they move to kiss again. They spring apart.

HERMIONE
Harry, Ginny and – I, uh – Draco – how lovely to see you—

HARRY
The dreams. They've started again, well, they haven't
stopped.

GINNY
And Albus is missing. Again.

DRACO
Scorpius too. We've had McGonagall check the entire
school. They're gone.

HERMIONE
I'll get the Aurors summoned immediately, I'll—

RON
No, you won't, it's all fine. Albus, I saw him last night. It's
all good.

DRACO
Where?

They all turn to look at RON, *he's briefly disconcerted but*
batters on.

RON
I was having a couple of Firewhiskies with Neville in

Hogsmeade – as you do – setting the world to rights – as we do – and we were coming back – quite late, very late, and trying to work out which Floo I could use because when you've had a drink sometimes you don't want to use the tight ones – or the turny ones or—

GINNY

Ron, if you could get to the point before we all strangle you?

RON

He hasn't run away – he's having a quiet moment – he's got himself an older girlfriend—

HARRY

An older girlfriend?

RON

And a cracking one at that – gorgeous silver hair. Saw them on the roof together, near the owlery with *Scrupious* playing the gooseberry. Nice to see my love potion being used well, I thought.

> HARRY *has a thought. And then he has a dozen more.*
> *And none of the thoughts are good.*

HARRY

Her hair – was it silver and blue?

RON

That's it – silver, blue – yup.

HARRY

He's talking about Delphi Diggory. Niece of – Amos Diggory.

GINNY

This is about Cedric again?

> HERMIONE *shouts out of the door.*

HERMIONE

Ethel. Cancel the goblins.

ACT THREE SCENE EIGHTEEN

ST OSWALD'S HOME FOR OLD WITCHES AND WIZARDS, AMOS'S ROOM

HARRY *walks in, wand outstretched, with* DRACO.

HARRY
Where are they?

AMOS
Harry Potter, and what can I do for you sir? And Draco
Malfoy. I am blessed.

HARRY
I know how you've used my son.

AMOS
I've used your son? No. You sir – you used my beautiful son.

DRACO
Tell us – now – where are Albus and Scorpius or face the
profoundest consequences.

AMOS
But why would I know where they are?

DRACO
Don't play the senility card with us, old man. We know
you've been sending him owls.

AMOS
I've done nothing of the kind.

HARRY

Amos, you're not too old for Azkaban. They were last
seen on the Hogwarts tower with your niece when they
disappeared.

AMOS

I have no idea what you are ... (*He stops, a beat, confused.*)
My niece?

HARRY

There are no depths to which you won't sink are there –
yes, your niece, are you denying she was there under your
express instructions ...

AMOS

Yes, I am – I don't have a niece.

This stops HARRY.

DRACO

Yes, you do, a nurse, works here. Your niece ... Delphini
Diggory.

AMOS

I know I don't have a niece because I never had any
brothers and sisters. And nor did my wife.

HARRY *and* DRACO *look at each other – both realising
what this means.*

DRACO

We need to find out who she is – *now.*

ACT THREE   SCENE NINETEEN

HOGWARTS, QUIDDITCH PITCH

We open on DELPHI, *enjoying every second of her changed identity. Where there was discomfort and insecurity, now there's just strength.*

ALBUS

What are we doing on the Quidditch pitch?

SCORPIUS *calculates rapidly.*

SCORPIUS

The Triwizard Tournament. The third task. The maze. This is where the maze was. We're going back for Cedric.

DELPHI

Yes, it is time to spare the spare once and for all. We will go back for Cedric and in doing so we will resurrect the world you saw Scorpius . . .

SCORPIUS

Hell. You want to resurrect hell?

DELPHI

I want a return to pure and strong magic. I want to rebirth the Dark.

SCORPIUS

You want Voldemort's return?

DELPHI

The one true ruler of the wizarding world. He will return.

Beat.

Now you've ensured the first two tasks are a little clogged up with magic – there are at least two visits from the future in both of them and I will not risk being revealed or distracted. The third task is clean, so let's start there, shall we?

ALBUS

We won't stop him – whatever you force us to do – we know he needs to win the tournament with my dad.

DELPHI

I don't just want you to stop him. I want you to humiliate him. He needs to fly out of that maze naked on a broomstick made of purple feather dusters. Humiliation got you there before and it'll get us there again. And the prophecy will be fulfilled.

SCORPIUS

Wasn't aware that there was a prophecy – what prophecy?

DELPHI

You have seen the world as it should be Scorpius, and today we're going to ensure its return.

ALBUS

We won't. We won't obey you. Whoever you are. Whatever you want us to do.

DELPHI

Of course you will.

ALBUS

You'll have to use Imperio. You'll have to control me.

DELPHI

No. To fulfil the prophecy, this has to be you, not a puppet of you . . . you have to be the one to humiliate Cedric, so Imperio just won't do – I'll have to force you by other means.

She takes out her wand. She points it at ALBUS, *who sticks his chin out.*

ALBUS
    Do your worst.

> DELPHI *looks at him. And then turns her wand on*
> SCORPIUS.

DELPHI
    I will.

ALBUS
    No!

DELPHI
    Yes, as I thought – this seems to frighten you more.

SCORPIUS
    Albus, whatever she does to me – we can't let her—

DELPHI
    Crucio!

> SCORPIUS *yells out in pain.*

ALBUS
    I will ...

DELPHI *(laughing)*
    What? What on earth do you think you can do? A
    wizardwide disappointment? A sore on your family name? A
    spare? You want to stop me hurting your only friend? Then
    do what you're told.

> *She looks at* ALBUS. *His eyes stay resistant.*

No? Crucio!

ALBUS
    Stop! Please.

> CRAIG *runs in, full of energy.*

CRAIG BOWKER JR
    Scorpius? Albus? Everyone's looking for you—

ALBUS
    Craig! Get away. Get help!

CRAIG BOWKER JR
What's happening?

DELPHI
Avada Kedavra!

>DELPHI *sends a blast of green light across the stage.* CRAIG
>*is propelled backwards by it – and is immediately killed.*
>*There's a silence. A silence that seems to last for a long*
>*time.*

Did you not understand? These are not childish games
we are playing here. You are useful to me, your friends are
not.

>ALBUS *and* SCORPIUS *look at* CRAIG's *body – their minds in*
>*torment.*

It took me a long time to discover your weakness, Albus
Potter. I thought it was pride, I thought it was the need to
impress your father, but then I realised your weakness was
the same as your father's – friendship. You will do exactly as
you're told, otherwise Scorpius will die, just like that *spare*
did.

>*She looks at them both.*

Voldemort will return and the Augurey will sit at his side.
Just as it was prophesied. 'When spares are spared, when
time is turned, when unseen children murder their fathers:
then will the Dark Lord return.'

>*She smiles. She pulls* SCORPIUS *viciously towards her.*

Cedric is the spare, and Albus—

>*She pulls* ALBUS *viciously towards her.*

—the unseen child who will kill his father by rewriting
time and so return the Dark Lord.

The Time-Turner starts rotating. She pulls their hands to it.

Now!

And there is a giant whoosh of light. A smash of noise.
And time stops. And then it turns over, thinks a bit, and begins spooling backwards, slow at first . . .
And then it speeds up.
And then there's a sucking noise. And a bang.

———

ACT THREE   SCENE TWENTY

TRIWIZARD TOURNAMENT, MAZE, 1995

The maze is a spiral of hedges that don't stop moving. DELPHI *walks determinedly through it. Behind her she drags* ALBUS *and* SCORPIUS. *Their arms bound, their legs reluctantly moving.*

LUDO BAGMAN
Ladies and gentlemen, boys and girls, I give you –
the greatest – the fabulous – the one – and the only
TRIWIZARD TOURNAMENT!

There's a loud cheer. DELPHI *turns left.*

If you're from Hogwarts. Give me a cheer.

There's a loud cheer.

If you're from Durmstrang – give me a cheer.

There's a loud cheer.

AND IF YOU'RE FROM BEAUXBATONS GIVE ME A
CHEER.

There's a fulsome cheer.
DELPHI *and the boys are forced to move as a hedge closes upon them.*

The French finally showing us what they're capable of

there. Ladies and gentlemen, I give you – the final of
the Triwizard tasks. A maze of mysteries, a disease of
uncontrollable darkness, for this maze – it lives. It lives.

*VIKTOR KRUM passes across the stage, moving through the
maze.*

And why risk this living nightmare? Because inside this
maze is a Cup – and not just any Cup – yes, the Triwizard
trophy stands within this vegetation.

DELPHI
Where is he? Where is Cedric?

A hedge almost dissects ALBUS and SCORPIUS.

SCORPIUS
The hedges want to kill us too? This gets better and better.

DELPHI
You will keep up or face the consequences.

LUDO BAGMAN
The perils are plentiful, but the prizes are palpable. Who
will fight their way through? Who will fall at the final
hurdle? What heroes do we have within our midst? Only
time will tell, ladies and gentlemen, only time will tell.

*They move through the maze, SCORPIUS and ALBUS being
compelled by DELPHI. As she moves ahead, the boys have
a chance to talk.*

SCORPIUS
Albus, we need to do something.

ALBUS
I know but what? She has snapped our wands, we're bound
and she's threatening to kill you.

SCORPIUS
I'm ready to die if it'll stop Voldemort returning.

ALBUS
Are you?

SCORPIUS

You won't have to mourn me for long, she'll kill me and quickly kill you too.

ALBUS (*desperate*)

The flaw in the Time-Turner, the five-minute rule. We do all we can to run down the clock.

SCORPIUS

It won't work.

> *As another hedge changes direction,* DELPHI *pulls* ALBUS *and* SCORPIUS *in after her. They continue through this maze of despair.*

LUDO BAGMAN

Now let me remind you of the current standings! Tied in first place – Mr Cedric Diggory and Mr Harry Potter. In second place – Mr Viktor Krum! And in third place – sacré bleu, Miss Fleur Delacour.

> *Suddenly,* ALBUS *and* SCORPIUS *emerge from behind a maze, they're running.*

ALBUS

Where did she go?

SCORPIUS

Does it matter? Which way do you think?

> DELPHI *rises up after them. She's flying, and without a broom.*

DELPHI

You poor creatures.

> *She throws the boys to the ground.*

Thinking you can escape me.

ALBUS (*astonished*)

You're not – even on a broom.

DELPHI

> Brooms – such unwieldy unnecessary objects. Three minutes gone. We have two minutes left. And you will do what you're told.

SCORPIUS

> No. We won't.

DELPHI

> You think you can fight me?

SCORPIUS

> No. But we can defy you. If we lay down our lives to do so.

DELPHI

> The prophecy must be fulfilled. We will fulfil it.

SCORPIUS

> Prophecies can be broken.

DELPHI

> You're mistaken child, prophecies are the future.

SCORPIUS

> But if the prophecy is inevitable why are we here trying to influence it? Your actions contradict your thoughts: you're dragging us through this maze because you believe this prophecy needs to be enabled – and, by that logic, prophecies can also be broken – prevented.

DELPHI

> You talk too much, child. Crucio!

> SCORPIUS *is racked with pain.*

ALBUS

> Scorpius!

SCORPIUS

> You wanted a test, Albus – this is it, and we're going to pass it.

> ALBUS *looks at* SCORPIUS, *finally aware what he has to do. He nods.*

DELPHI

> Then you will die.

ALBUS *(full of strength)*
Yes. We will. And we'll do so gladly knowing it's stopped you.

DELPHI rises up, full of fury.

DELPHI
We don't have time for this. Cru—

MYSTERIOUS VOICE
Expelliarmus!

Bang. DELPHI's wand is pulled away from her. SCORPIUS looks on in astonishment.

Brachiabindo!

And DELPHI is bound. SCORPIUS and ALBUS then turn as one and stare in astonishment at where the bolt came from: from a young, good-looking lad of seventeen or so, CEDRIC.

CEDRIC
Come no further.

SCORPIUS
But you're ...

CEDRIC
Cedric Diggory. I heard screaming, I had to come. Name yourselves, beasts, I can fight you.

ALBUS wheels around, astonished.

ALBUS
Cedric?

SCORPIUS
You saved us.

CEDRIC
Are you also a task? An obstacle? Speak. Do I have to defeat you too?

There's a silence.

SCORPIUS
No. You just have to free us. That's the task.

CEDRIC thinks, trying to work out whether it's a trap, and then waves his wand.

CEDRIC
Emancipare! Emancipare!

The boys are freed.

And now I can go on? Finish the maze?

The boys look at CEDRIC – they know exactly what it means for him to finish the maze.

ALBUS
I'm afraid you have to finish the maze.

CEDRIC
Then I shall.

CEDRIC walks confidently away. ALBUS looks after him – desperate to say something, unsure what to say.

ALBUS
Cedric—

CEDRIC turns towards him.

Your dad loves you very much.

CEDRIC frowns, surprised.

CEDRIC
What?

Behind them, DELPHI's body creeps into movement. She crawls along the ground.

ALBUS
Just thought you should know that.

CEDRIC *(struggling how to process this)*
Okay. Um. Thank you.

CEDRIC *looks at* ALBUS *a moment more, and then walks on. As he does so,* DELPHI *pulls out the Time-Turner from within her robes and* SCORPIUS *sees her.*

SCORPIUS
Albus!

ALBUS
No. Wait . . .

SCORPIUS
The Time Turner is spinning . . . look at what she's doing . . . she can't leave us behind.

ALBUS *and* SCORPIUS *both scramble to grab part of the Time-Turner.*

And there is a giant whoosh of light. A smash of noise.

And time stops. And then it turns over, thinks a bit, and begins spooling backwards, slow at first . . .

And then it speeds up.

Albus . . .

ALBUS
What have we done?

SCORPIUS
We had to go with the Time-Turner, we had to try to stop her.

DELPHI
Stop me? How do you think you've stopped me? I am done with this.

She crushes the Time-Turner. It explodes into a thousand pieces.

You may have destroyed my chances of using Cedric to darken the world but maybe you're right Scorpius – maybe prophecies can be prevented, maybe prophecies can be broken. What is undoubtedly true is I'm done with trying to use you annoying, incompetent creatures for anything. No more wasting precious seconds on either of you. Time to try something new.

DELPHI *ascends again into the air. She laughs in delight as she sets off, hard away.*

The boys try to chase her, but they've not the slightest chance. She flies, they run.

ALBUS

No ... no ... you can't ...

SCORPIUS *turns back and tries to pick up the Time-Turner pieces.*

The Time-Turner? It's destroyed?

SCORPIUS

Utterly. We're stuck here. In time. Wherever in time we are. Whatever it is she's planning to do.

ALBUS *looks around, trying desperately to process what's just happened.*

ALBUS

Hogwarts looks the same.

SCORPIUS

Yes. And we can't be seen here. Let's get out of here before we're spotted.

ALBUS

We need to stop her, Scorpius.

SCORPIUS

I know we do – but how?

ACT THREE   SCENE TWENTY-ONE

ST OSWALD'S HOME FOR OLD WITCHES AND WIZARDS, DELPHI'S ROOM

HARRY, HERMIONE, RON, DRACO *and* GINNY *look around a simple oak-panelled room.*

HARRY
It must have been a Confundus Charm she used on him. Used on them all. She faked being a nurse, she faked being his niece.

HERMIONE
I've just checked in with the Ministry – but there's no record of her. She's a shadow.

DRACO
Specialis Revelio!

Everyone turns to look at DRACO. *He looks back dryly.*

Well, it was worth a try, what are you waiting for? We know nothing, so we just have to hope this room reveals something.

GINNY
Where can she have hidden anything? It's quite a spartan room.

RON
These panels, these panels must conceal something.

DRACO
Or the bed.

> DRACO *starts examining the bed,* GINNY *a lamp, as the rest start examining the panels.*

RON *(shouting as he hammers on the walls)*
What you hiding? What you got?

HERMIONE
Maybe we should all stop for a moment and have a think about what—

> GINNY *unscrews a lamp chimney from an oil lamp. There's a breathing-out noise. And then hissing words. They all turn towards it.*

What was that?

HARRY
That's – I'm not supposed to be understanding – that's Parseltongue.

HERMIONE
And what does it say?

HARRY
How do I ... ? I haven't been able to understand Parseltongue since Voldemort died.

HERMIONE
And nor has your scar hurt.

> HARRY *looks at* HERMIONE.

HARRY
It says 'welcome Augurey'. I think I need to tell it to open ...

DRACO
Then do it.

> HARRY *shuts his eyes. He speaks in Parseltongue.*
> *The room transforms around them, becoming darker, and more desperate. A writhing mass of painted snakes emerges on all the walls.*

And on them, written in fluorescent paint, a prophecy.

What is this?

RON
'When spares are spared, when time is turned, when unseen children murder their fathers: then will the Dark Lord return.'

GINNY
A prophecy. A new prophecy.

HERMIONE
Cedric – Cedric was called a spare.

RON
When time is turned – she has that Time-Turner doesn't she?

Their faces sink.

HERMIONE
She must do.

RON
But why does she need Scorpius or Albus?

HARRY
Because I'm a parent – who hasn't seen his child. Hasn't understood his child.

DRACO
Who is she? To be so obsessed with all this?

GINNY
I think I've got the answer to that.

They all turn to her. She points up . . . their collective faces sink further and fill with fear.

Words are revealed on all the walls of the auditorium – dangerous words, horrible words.

'I will rebirth the Dark. I will bring my father back.'

RON
No. She can't . . .

HERMIONE
How is it even – possible?

DRACO
Voldemort had a daughter?

They look up terrified. GINNY *takes* HARRY's *hand.*

HARRY
No, no, no. Not that. Anything but that.

We cut to black.

INTERVAL

PART TWO
ACT FOUR

ACT FOUR   SCENE ONE

MINISTRY OF MAGIC, GRAND MEETING ROOM

Wizards and witches from all over cram into the grand meeting room. More than we've ever seen before. And their worry is writ large across their faces. HERMIONE *walks on to a hastily made stage. She raises her hand for silence. Silence falls; they're anxious for any answers she might give. She's surprised at the lack of effort it took. She looks around herself.*

HERMIONE

Thank you. I'm so pleased so many of you were able to make my – second – Extraordinary General Meeting. I've got some things to say – I ask that we deal with questions – and there will be a lot of questions – after I speak.

As many of you know, a body has been found at Hogwarts. His name was Craig Bowker. He was a good boy. We have no firm information who was responsible for the act but yesterday we searched St Oswald's. A room there revealed two things: one, a prophecy that promised . . . the return of darkness – two, written on the ceiling, a proclamation – that the Dark Lord had a – that Voldemort had a child.

The news reverberates around the room.

We don't know the full details. We're only just investigating – questioning those with a Death Eater connection ... and as yet no record has been found either of the child or of the prophecy, but, it does look like there's some truth to it. This child was kept hidden from the wizarding world, and now she's – well now she's—

PROFESSOR MCGONAGALL

She? A daughter? He had a daughter?

HERMIONE

Yes. A daughter.

PROFESSOR MCGONAGALL

And is she now in custody?

HARRY

Professor, she did ask for no questions.

HERMIONE

It's fine, Harry. No, Professor, that's where this gets worse. I'm afraid we've no means of taking her into custody. Or indeed, stopping her doing anything. She's out of our reach.

PROFESSOR MCGONAGALL

We can't – look for her?

There's a beat. This takes courage.

HERMIONE

We have good reason to believe she's hidden herself – in time.

PROFESSOR MCGONAGALL (*furious*)

Of all the reckless stupid things, you've kept the Time-Turner even now?

HERMIONE

Professor, I assure you—

PROFESSOR MCGONAGALL

Shame on you, Hermione Granger!

HERMIONE *flinches in the face of the anger.*

HARRY

No, she doesn't deserve that. You have a right to be angry. You all do. But this is not all Hermione's fault. We don't

know how the witch got hold of the Time-Turner. Whether
my son gave it to her.

GINNY
Whether our son gave it her. Or whether it was stolen from
him.

GINNY *joins* HARRY *on the stage.*

PROFESSOR MCGONAGALL
Your solidarity is admirable, but it doesn't make your
negligence negligible.

DRACO
Then it's a negligence I too should face.

DRACO *walks up to the stage and stands beside* GINNY.
This is almost a Spartacus moment. There are gasps.

Hermione and Harry have done nothing wrong but try and
protect us all. If they're guilty, then I am too.

HERMIONE *looks across at her cohort – moved.* RON
determinedly joins them on the stage.

RON
Just to say – I didn't know about much of it so can't take
responsibility – and I'm pretty sure my kids had nothing
to do with it – but if this lot are standing up here, then *so
am I.*

GINNY
No one can know where they are – whether they're
together or apart. I trust that our sons will be doing all they
can to stop her but . . .

HERMIONE
We haven't given up. We've gone to the giants. The trolls.
Everyone we can find. The Aurors are out flying, searching,
talking to those who know secrets, following those who
won't reveal secrets.

HARRY
But there is one truth we can't escape: that somewhere

in our past a witch is trying to rewrite everything we ever knew – and all we can do is wait – wait for the moment she either succeeds or fails.

PROFESSOR MCGONAGALL
And if she succeeds?

HERMIONE
Then – just like that – most of the people in this room will be gone, we'll no longer exist and Voldemort will rule again.

ACT FOUR   SCENE TWO

SCOTTISH HIGHLANDS, AVIEMORE TRAIN STATION, 1981

ALBUS *and* SCORPIUS *are looking at a* STATION MASTER, *apprehensively.*

ALBUS
One of us should talk to him, don't you think?

SCORPIUS
Hello, Mr Station Master. Mr Muggle. Question: did you
see a flying witch passing here? And by the way, what year
is it? We just ran away from Hogwarts because we were
frightened of upsetting things, but this is okay?

ALBUS
You know what annoys me most of all? Dad will think we
did it deliberately.

SCORPIUS
Albus. Really? I mean, *really* really? We're – trapped – lost –
in time – probably permanently – and you're worrying what
your dad might think about it? I will never understand the
two of you.

ALBUS
There's a lot to understand. Dad's pretty complicated.

SCORPIUS
And you're not? Not to question your taste in women but
you fancied ... well ...

They both know who he's talking about.

ALBUS
    I did, didn't I? I mean what she did to Craig . . .

SCORPIUS
    Let's not think about that. Let's focus on the fact that we
    have no wands, no brooms, no means of returning to our
    time, all we have is our wits and – no, that's all, our wits –
    and we have to stop her.

STATION MASTER *(in very strong Scots)*
    Ye ken th' Auld Reekie train is running late, boys?

SCORPIUS
    Sorry?

STATION MASTER
    If you're waiting oan th' Auld Reekie train, you'll need tae
    ken it's running late. Train wirks oan th' line. It's a' oan th'
    amended time buird.

    *He looks at them, they look back bewildered. He frowns
    and hands them an amended timetable. He points to the
    right bit of it.*

Late.

    ALBUS *takes it and examines it. His face changes as he
    takes in enormous information.* SCORPIUS *just stares at
    the Station Master.*

ALBUS
    I know where she is.

SCORPIUS
    You understood that?

ALBUS
    Look at the date. On the timetable.

    SCORPIUS *leans in and reads.*

SCORPIUS
    The thirtieth of October 1981. Day before Hallows' Eve,
    thirty-nine years ago. But – why is she? Oh.

SCORPIUS's *face falls as he realises.*

ALBUS
The death of my grandparents. The attack on my dad as a baby . . . the moment when Voldemort's curse rebounded on himself. She's not trying to bring about her prophecy – she's trying to prevent the big one.

SCORPIUS
The big one?

ALBUS
'The one with the power to vanquish the Dark Lord approaches . . .

SCORPIUS *joins in.*

SCORPIUS *and* **ALBUS**
'. . . born to those who have thrice defied him, born as the seventh month dies . . .'

SCORPIUS's *face falls with every word.*

SCORPIUS
It's my fault. I told her that prophecies can be broken – I told her the whole logic of prophecies is questionable—

ALBUS
In twenty-four hours' time Voldemort curses himself trying to kill the baby Harry Potter. Delphi is trying to prevent that curse. She's going to kill Harry herself. We need to get to Godric's Hollow. Now.

ACT FOUR   SCENE THREE

GODRIC'S HOLLOW, 1981

ALBUS *and* SCORPIUS *walk through the centre of Godric's Hollow and it's a bustling, beautiful little village.*

SCORPIUS
Well, there's no visible signs of attack that I can see . . .

ALBUS
This is Godric's Hollow?

SCORPIUS
Your dad's never taken you?

ALBUS
No, he tried to a few times but I refused.

SCORPIUS
Well there's no time for a tour – we have a murderous witch to save the world from – but regard . . . the church, St Jerome's . . .

As he indicates a church becomes visible.

ALBUS
It's magnificent.

SCORPIUS
And St Jerome's graveyard is supposedly magnificently haunted (*he points in another direction*), and that's where the statue of Harry and his parents will be—

ALBUS
My dad has a statue?

SCORPIUS
Oh. Not yet. But he will. Hopefully. And this – this house is where Bathilda Bagshot lived, lives . . .

ALBUS
The Bathilda Bagshot? *A History of Magic* Bathilda Bagshot?

SCORPIUS
The very same. Oh my, that's her. Wow. Squeak. My geekness is a-quivering.

ALBUS
Scorpius!

SCORPIUS
And here it is—

ALBUS
The home of James, Lily and Harry Potter . . .

A young, attractive couple leave a house with a baby in a pushchair. ALBUS *moves towards them,* SCORPIUS *pulls him back.*

SCORPIUS
They can't see you, Albus, it might damage time, and we're not doing that – not this time.

ALBUS
But this means, she hasn't . . . we've made it . . . she hasn't . . .

SCORPIUS
So what do we do now? Get ready to fight her? Because she's pretty . . . fierce.

ALBUS
Yes. We haven't really thought this one through have we? What do we do now? How do we protect my dad?

ACT FOUR   SCENE FOUR

MINISTRY OF MAGIC, HARRY'S OFFICE

HARRY *is hurriedly going through paperwork.*

DUMBLEDORE
Good evening, Harry.

> *Beat.* HARRY *looks up at the portrait of* DUMBLEDORE, *his face passive.*

HARRY
Professor Dumbledore. In my office, I'm honoured. I must be where the action is, tonight?

DUMBLEDORE
What are you doing?

HARRY
Going through papers, seeing if I've missed anything I shouldn't have. Marshalling forces to fight in the limited way we can fight. Knowing that the battle is being raged far away from us. What else can I do?

> *Pause.* DUMBLEDORE *says nothing.*

Where have you been, Dumbledore?

DUMBLEDORE
I'm here now.

HARRY

Here just as the battle is lost. Or are you denying that
Voldemort is going to return?

DUMBLEDORE

It is – possible.

HARRY

Go. Leave. I don't want you here, I don't need you. You
were absent every time it really counted. I fought him three
times without you. I'll face him again, if needs be – alone.

DUMBLEDORE

Harry, don't you think I wanted to fight him on your
behalf? I would have spared you if I could—

At that HARRY *erupts.*

HARRY

Love blinds us? Do you even know what that means? Do
you even know how bad that advice was? My son is – my
son is fighting battles for us just as I had to for you. And
I have proved as bad a father to him as you were to me.
Leaving him in places he felt unloved – growing in him
resentments he'll take years to understand—

DUMBLEDORE

If you're referring to Privet Drive then—

HARRY

Years – years I spent there alone, without knowing what
I was, or why I was there, without knowing that anybody
cared!

DUMBLEDORE

I – did not wish to become attached to you—

HARRY

Protecting yourself, even then!

DUMBLEDORE

No. I was protecting you. I did not want to hurt you . . .

DUMBLEDORE *attempts to reach out of the portrait, but he
can't. He begins to cry but tries to hide it.*

But I had to meet you in the end ... eleven years old, and you were so brave. So good. You walked uncomplainingly along the path that had been laid at your feet. Of course I loved you ... and I knew that it would happen all over again ... that where I loved, I would cause irreparable damage ... I am no fit person to love ... I have never loved without causing harm ...

Beat.

HARRY
You would have hurt me less if you had told me this, then.

DUMBLEDORE (*openly weeping now*)
I was blind. That is what love does. I couldn't see that you needed to hear that this closed-up, tricky, dangerous old man ... loved you ...

A pause. The two men are overcome with emotion.

HARRY
It isn't true that I never complained.

DUMBLEDORE
Harry, there is never a perfect answer in this messy, emotional world. Perfection is beyond the reach of humankind, beyond the reach of magic. In every shining moment of happiness is that drop of poison: the knowledge that pain will come again. Be honest to those you love, show them your pain. To suffer is as human as to breathe.

HARRY
You said that to me once before.

DUMBLEDORE
It is all I have to offer you tonight.

He begins to walk away.

HARRY
Don't go!

DUMBLEDORE
Those that we love never truly leave us, Harry. There are

things that death cannot touch. Paint . . . and memory . . .
and love.

HARRY
I loved you too, Dumbledore.

DUMBLEDORE
I know.

He is gone. And HARRY *is alone.* DRACO *enters.*

DRACO
Did you know that in this other reality – the reality
Scorpius saw into – I was Head of Magical Law
Enforcement? Maybe this room will be mine soon enough.
Are you okay?

HARRY *is consumed in his grief.*

HARRY
Come in – I'll give you the tour.

DRACO *walks hesitantly inside the room. He looks around
distastefully.*

DRACO
The thing is though – never really fancied being a Ministry
man. Even as a child. My dad – it's all he ever wanted – me, no.

HARRY
What did you want to do?

DRACO
Quidditch. But I wasn't good enough. Mainly I wanted to
be happy.

HARRY *nods.* DRACO *looks at him a second more, unsure
how to do this.*

Sorry, I'm not very good at small talk, do you mind if we
skip on to the serious business?

HARRY
Of course. What – serious – business?

Beat.

DRACO

Do you think Theodore Nott had the only Time-Turner?

HARRY

What?

DRACO

The Time-Turner the Ministry seized was a prototype. Made of inexpensive metal. It does the job, sure. But only being able to go back in time for five minutes – that's a serious flaw – it isn't something you'd sell to true collectors of Dark Magic.

HARRY *realises what* DRACO *is saying.*

HARRY

He was working for you?

DRACO

No. My father. He liked owning things that no one else had. The Ministry's Time-Turners – thanks to Croaker – were always a little vanilla for him. He wanted the ability to go back further than an hour, he wanted the ability to travel back years. He'd never have used it, secretly I think he preferred a world without Voldemort. But yes, the Time-Turner was built for him.

HARRY

And did you keep it?

DRACO *reveals the Time-Turner.*

DRACO

No five-minute problem, and it gleams like gold, just the way the Malfoys like it. You're smiling.

HARRY

Hermione Granger. It was the reason she kept the first, the fear that there might be a second. Hanging on to this, you could have been sent to Azkaban.

DRACO

Consider the alternative – consider if people had known that I had the ability to travel in time. Consider the rumour that would have been given increased – credence.

HARRY *looks at* DRACO, *understanding him perfectly.*

HARRY

Scorpius.

DRACO

We were capable of having children, but Astoria was
frail. A blood malediction, a serious one. An ancestor was
cursed . . . it showed up in her. You know how these things
can resurface after generations . . .

HARRY

I'm sorry, Draco.

DRACO

I didn't want to risk her health, I said it didn't matter
whether the Malfoy line died with me – whatever my
father said. But Astoria – she didn't want a baby for the
Malfoy name, for pure blood or glory, but for us. Our child,
Scorpius was born . . . it was the best day of both our
lives, although it weakened Astoria considerably. We hid
ourselves away, the three of us. I wanted to conserve her
strength . . . and so the rumours started.

HARRY

I can't imagine what that was like.

DRACO

Astoria always knew that she was not destined for old
age. She wanted me to have somebody when she left,
because . . . it is exceptionally lonely, being Draco Malfoy.
I will always be suspected. There is no escaping the past. I
never realised, though, that by hiding him away from this
gossiping, judgemental world, I ensured that my son would
emerge shrouded in worse suspicion than I ever endured.

HARRY

Love blinds. We have both tried to give our sons not what
they needed, but what we needed. We've been so busy
trying to rewrite our own pasts, we've blighted their
present.

DRACO

Which is why you need this. I have been holding on to it, barely resisting using it, even though I would sell my soul for another minute with Astoria . . .

HARRY

Oh, Draco . . . we can't. We can't use it.

DRACO *looks up at* HARRY, *and for the first time – at the bottom of this dreadful pit – they look at each other as friends.*

DRACO

We have to find them – if it takes centuries, we must find our sons . . .

HARRY

We have no idea where they are or when they are. Searching in time when you've no idea where in time to search, that's a fool's errand. No, love won't do it and nor will a Time-Turner, I'm afraid. It's up to our sons now – they're the only ones who can save us.

ACT FOUR   SCENE FIVE

GODRIC'S HOLLOW, OUTSIDE JAMES AND
LILY POTTER'S HOUSE, 1981

ALBUS *and* SCORPIUS *look hopelessly around, trying to think themselves out of the most epic of problems.*

ALBUS
We tell my granddad and grandma?

SCORPIUS
That they'll never get to see their son grow up?

ALBUS
She's strong enough – I know she is – you saw her.

SCORPIUS
She looked wonderful, Albus. And if I were you I'd be desperate to talk to her. But she needs to be able to beg Voldemort for Harry's life, she needs to think he might die, and you're the worst spoiler in the world that didn't turn out to be true . . .

ALBUS
Dumbledore. Dumbledore's alive. We get Dumbledore involved. We do what you did with Snape—

SCORPIUS
Can we risk him knowing your dad survives? That he has kids?

ALBUS

He's Dumbledore! He can cope with anything!

SCORPIUS

Albus, there have been about a hundred books written on what Dumbledore knew, how he knew it or why he did what he did. But what's undoubtedly true – what he did – he needs to do – and I'm not going to risk messing with it. (*Beat, he looks imploringly at his friend.*) I was able to ask for help because I was in an alternate reality. We aren't. We're in the past. We can't fix time only to create more problems – if our adventures have taught us anything, they've taught us that. The dangers of talking to anyone – infecting time – are too great.

ALBUS

So we need to – talk to the future. We need to send Dad a message.

SCORPIUS

But we don't have an owl that can fly through time. And he doesn't have a Time-Turner.

ALBUS

We get a message to Dad. He'll find a way to get back here. Even if he has to build a Time-Turner himself.

SCORPIUS

We send a memory – like a Pensieve – stand over him and send a message, hope he reaches for the memory at exactly the right moment. I mean, it's unlikely, but ... stand over the baby – and just repeatedly shout HELP. HELP. HELP. I mean, it might traumatise the baby slightly.

ALBUS

Only slightly.

SCORPIUS

A bit of trauma now is nothing compared to what's happening ... and maybe when he then thinks – later – he might remember the faces of us as we – shouted—

ALBUS

Help.

SCORPIUS *looks at* ALBUS.

SCORPIUS

You're right. It's a terrible idea.

ALBUS

It's one of your worst ideas ever.

SCORPIUS

Got it! We deliver it ourselves – we wait forty years – we
deliver it—

ALBUS

Not a chance – once Delphi has set time the way she wants
she'll send armies to try and find us – kill us—

SCORPIUS

So we hide in a hole?

ALBUS

As pleasurable as it will be to hide in a hole with you for
the next forty years . . . they'll find us. And we'll die and
time will be stuck in the wrong position. No. We need
something we can control, something we know he'll get at
exactly the right time. We need a . . .

SCORPIUS

There's nothing. Still, if I had to choose a companion to be
at the return of eternal darkness with, I'd choose you.

ALBUS

No offence, but I'd choose someone massive and really good
at magic.

LILY *exits the house with* BABY HARRY *in a pram, she
carefully puts a blanket on him.*

His blanket. She's wrapping him in his blanket.

SCORPIUS

Well, it is a moderately cold day.

ALBUS

He always said – it's the only thing he had from her. Look
at the love with which she's put it on him – I think he'd like
to know about that – I wish I could tell him.

SCORPIUS

And I wish I could tell my dad – well, I'm not sure what.
I think I'd like to tell him that I'm occasionally capable of
more bravery than he might think I am.

ALBUS *has a thought.*

ALBUS

Scorpius – my dad still has that blanket.

SCORPIUS

That won't work. If we write a message on it now, even
really small, he'll read it too soon. Time will be spoilt.

ALBUS

What do you know about love potions? What's the
ingredient they all contain?

SCORPIUS

Amongst other things, Pearl Dust.

ALBUS

Pearl Dust is a relatively rare ingredient isn't it?

SCORPIUS

Mainly because it's pretty expensive. What's this about,
Albus?

ALBUS

Dad and I had a fight on the day before I went to school.

SCORPIUS

This I am aware of. I believe it kind of got us into this mess.

ALBUS

I threw the blanket across the room. It collided with the
love potion that Uncle Ron gave me as a joke. The potion
spilt and the blanket was covered in it and I happen to
know for a fact Mum hasn't let Dad touch that room since
I left it.

SCORPIUS

So?

ALBUS

So it's coming up to Hallows' Eve in their time as well as
ours – and he told me he always finds that blanket, he

needs to be with it on Hallows' Eve – it was the last thing
his mum gave him – so he will look for it and when he finds
it . . .

SCORPIUS

No. Still not getting you.

ALBUS

What reacts with Pearl Dust?

SCORPIUS

Well, it is said that if Tincture of Demiguise and Pearl Dust
meet . . . they burn.

ALBUS

And is Tincture of (*he's unsure how to say the word*)
Demiguise visible to the naked eye?

SCORPIUS

No.

ALBUS

So if we were to get that blanket and write on it in
Tincture of Demiguise then . . .

SCORPIUS (*eureka*)

Nothing would react to it until it came into contact
with the love potion. In your room. In the present. By
Dumbledore, I love it.

ALBUS

We just need to work out where to find some . . .
Demiguises.

SCORPIUS

You know, rumour has it Bathilda Bagshot never saw the
point in witches and wizards locking their doors.

The door swings open.

Rumour was right. Time to steal some wands and get
potioning.

ACT FOUR SCENE SIX

HARRY AND GINNY POTTER'S HOUSE, ALBUS'S ROOM

HARRY *is sitting on* ALBUS's *bed.* GINNY *enters, she looks at him.*

GINNY
Surprised to find you here.

HARRY
Don't worry, I haven't touched anything. Your shrine is preserved. (*He winces.*) Sorry. Bad choice of words.

GINNY *says nothing.* HARRY *looks up at her.*

You know I've had some pretty terrible Hallows' Eves – but this is undoubtedly at least the – second worst.

GINNY
I was wrong – to blame you – I always accuse you of jumping to things and it was me who – Albus went missing and I assumed it was your fault. I'm sorry I did that.

HARRY
You don't think this is my fault?

GINNY
Harry, he was kidnapped by a powerful Dark witch, how can that be your fault?

HARRY
I chased him away. I chased him to her.

GINNY
 Can we not treat this as if the battle is already lost?

GINNY nods. HARRY starts to cry.

HARRY
 I'm sorry Gin—

GINNY
 Are you not listening to me? I'm sorry too.

HARRY
 I shouldn't have survived – it was my destiny to die – even
 Dumbledore thought so – and yet I lived. I beat Voldemort.
 All these people – all these people – this boy Craig, my
 parents, Fred, the Fallen Fifty – and it's me that gets to live?
 How is that? All this damage – and it's my fault.

GINNY
 They were killed by Voldemort.

HARRY
 But if I'd stopped him sooner? All that blood on my hands.
 And now our son has been taken too—

GINNY
 He's not dead. Do you hear me Harry? He's not dead.

*She takes HARRY in her arms. There is a big pause filled
with pure unhappiness.*

HARRY
 The Boy Who Lived. How many people have to die for the
 Boy Who Lived?

*HARRY sways a moment, unsure. Then he notices the
blanket. He walks towards it.*

This blanket is all I have you know . . . of that Hallows' Eve.
This is all I have to remember them. And whilst—

*He picks up the blanket. He discovers it has holes in it.
He looks at it, dismayed.*

This has got holes in it. Ron's idiotic love potion has burnt through it, right through it. Look at this. It's ruined. Ruined.

He throws down the blanket. GINNY *picks it up, examining it.*

GINNY
Harry . . .

HARRY
What?

GINNY
Harry, it has – something – written—

And without warning, ALBUS *and* SCORPIUS *appear, sharing the stage with* HARRY *and* GINNY *even though they are separated by time.*

ALBUS
'Dad . . .'

SCORPIUS
We're starting with 'Dad'?

ALBUS
So he'll know it's from me.

SCORPIUS
Harry is his name. We should start with 'Harry'.

ALBUS *(firm)*
We're starting with 'Dad'.

HARRY
'Dad', does it say 'Dad'? It's not that distinct . . .

SCORPIUS
'Dad, HELP.'

GINNY
'Hello'? Does that say 'Hello'? And then . . . 'Good' . . .

HARRY
'Dad Hello Good Hello'? No. This is . . . a strange joke.

ALBUS
'Dad. Help. Godric's Hollow.'

GINNY

Give me that. My eyesight is better than yours. Yes. 'Dad
Hello Good' – that's not 'Hello' again – that's 'Hallow' or
'Hollow'? And then some numbers – these are clearer –
'3 . . . 1 . . . 1 . . . 0 . . . 8 . . . 1'. Is this one of those Muggle
telephone numbers? Or a grid reference or a . . .

*HARRY looks up, several thoughts smashing through his
brain at once.*

HARRY

No. It's a date. 31 October 1981. The date my parents were
killed.

GINNY looks at HARRY, and then back at the blanket.

GINNY

That doesn't say 'Hello'. It says 'Help'.

HARRY

'Dad. Help. Godric's Hollow. 31/10/81.' It's a message. Clever
boy left me a message.

HARRY kisses GINNY hard.

GINNY

Albus wrote this?

HARRY

And he's told me where they are and when they are, and
now we know where she is, we know where we can fight
her.

He kisses her hard again.

GINNY

We haven't got them back again yet.

HARRY

I'll send an owl to Hermione. You send one to Draco.
Tell them to meet us at Godric's Hollow with the
Time-Turner.

GINNY

And it is 'us', okay? Don't even think about going back
without me, Harry.

HARRY *kisses his wife – full of gratitude and love.*

HARRY

Of course you're coming. We have a chance Ginny, and by
Dumbledore – that's all that we need – a chance.

ACT FOUR   SCENE SEVEN

GODRIC'S HOLLOW

RON, HERMIONE, DRACO, HARRY *and* GINNY *walk through a present-day Godric's Hollow. A busy market town (it's expanded over the years).*

HERMIONE
Godric's Hollow. It must be twenty years . . .

GINNY
Is it just me or are there more Muggles about?

HERMIONE
It's become quite popular as a weekend break.

DRACO
I can see why – look at the thatched roofs. And is that a farmers' market?

> HERMIONE *approaches* HARRY *– who is looking around himself, overwhelmed by all he is seeing.*

HERMIONE
You remember when we were last here? This feels just like old times.

RON
Old times with a few unwelcome ponytails added to the mix.

> DRACO *knows a barb when he hears one.*

DRACO

Can I just say . . .

RON

Malfoy, you may be all chummy chummy with Harry, and you may have produced a relatively nice child, but you've said some very unfair things to and about my wife . . .

HERMIONE

And your wife doesn't need you fighting her battles for her.

HERMIONE *looks witheringly at* RON. RON *takes the hit.*

RON

Fine. But if you say one thing about her or me . . .

DRACO

You'll do what, Weasley?

HERMIONE

He'll hug you. Because we're all on the same team, aren't we Ron?

RON *(hesitating in the face of her unwavering gaze)*

Fine. I, um, I think you've got really nice hair. Draco.

HERMIONE

Thank you, husband. Now this seems a good spot. Let's do this . . .

DRACO *takes out the Time-Turner – it begins spinning wildly as the others take their places around it.*

And there is a giant whoosh of light. A smash of noise.

And time stops. And then it turns over, thinks a bit, and begins spooling backwards, slow at first . . .

And then it speeds up.

They look around themselves.

RON

So? Has it worked?

ACT FOUR   SCENE EIGHT

GODRIC'S HOLLOW, A SHED, 1981

ALBUS *looks up amazed to see* GINNY *and then* HARRY, *and then he takes in the rest of the happy band (*RON, DRACO *and* HERMIONE*).*

ALBUS
MUM?

HARRY
Albus Severus Potter. Are we pleased to see you.

> ALBUS *runs and throws himself into* GINNY'S *arms.* GINNY *receives him, delighted.*

ALBUS
You got our note . . . ?

GINNY
We got your note.

> SCORPIUS *trots up to his dad.*

DRACO
We can hug too if you like . . .

> SCORPIUS *looks at his dad, unsure for a moment. And then they sort of half-hug in a very awkward way.* DRACO *smiles.*

RON
Now, where's this Delphi?

SCORPIUS

You know about Delphi?

ALBUS

She's here – she's trying to kill you we think. Before
Voldemort curses himself. She's going to kill you and so
break the prophecy and . . .

HERMIONE

Yes, we thought that might be it too. Do you know where
specifically she is now?

SCORPIUS

She's disappeared. How did you – how did you without the
Time-Turner . . .

HARRY (*interrupting*)

That's a long and complicated story, Scorpius. And we don't
have time for it.

> DRACO *smiles at* HARRY *gratefully.*

HERMIONE

Harry's right. Time is of the essence. We need to get people
into position. Now, Godric's Hollow is not a large place,
but she could be coming from any direction. So we need
somewhere that gives us good views of the town – that
allows for multiple and clear observation points – and that
will, most importantly, keep us hidden because we cannot
risk being seen.

> *They all frown, thinking.*

I'd say St Jerome's Church ticks all those boxes wouldn't
you?

ACT FOUR   SCENE NINE

GODRIC'S HOLLOW, CHURCH, SANCTUARY, 1981

ALBUS *is sleeping in a pew.* GINNY *watches him carefully.* HARRY *is looking out the opposite window.*

HARRY

No. Nothing. Why isn't she here?

GINNY

We're together, your mum and dad are alive, we can turn time Harry, we can't speed it up. She'll come when she's ready and we'll be ready for her.

She looks at ALBUS's *sleeping form.*

Or some of us will be.

HARRY

Poor kid thought he had to save the world.

GINNY

Poor kid has saved the world. That blanket was masterful. I mean, he also almost destroyed the world, but probably best not to focus on that bit.

HARRY

You think he's okay?

GINNY

He's getting there, it just might take him a bit of time – and you a bit of time too.

HARRY *smiles. She looks back at* ALBUS. *He does too.*

You know, after I'd opened the Chamber of Secrets – after
Voldemort had bewitched me with that terrible diary and
I'd almost destroyed everything—

HARRY

I remember.

GINNY

After I came out of hospital – everyone ignored me, shut
me out – other than, that is, the boy who had everything –
who came across the Gryffindor common room and
challenged me to a game of Exploding Snap. People think
they know all there is to know about you, but the best bits
of you are – have always been – heroic in really quiet ways.
My point is – after this is over, just remember if you could –
that sometimes people – but particularly children – just
want someone to play Exploding Snap with.

HARRY

You think that's what we're missing – Exploding Snap?

GINNY

No. But the love I felt from you that day – I'm not sure
Albus feels that.

HARRY

I'd do anything for him.

GINNY

Harry, you'd do anything for anybody. You were pretty
happy to sacrifice yourself for the world. He needs to feel
specific love. It'll make him stronger, and you stronger too.

HARRY

You know, it wasn't until we thought Albus had gone that I
truly understood what my mother was able to do for me. A
counter-charm so powerful that it was able to repel the spell
of death.

GINNY

And the only spell Voldemort couldn't understand – love.

The word feels both heavy and beautiful in the room.

HARRY
I do love him specifically, Ginny.

GINNY
I know, but he needs to feel it.

HARRY *smiles sadly at his wife, aware of all he needs to change.*

HARRY
I'm lucky to have you aren't I?

GINNY
Extremely. And I'd be delighted to discuss just how lucky at another time. But for now – let's focus on stopping Delphi.

HARRY
We are running out of time.

A thought occurs to GINNY.

GINNY
Unless – Harry, has anyone thought – why has she picked now? Today?

HARRY
Because this is the day that everything changed . . .

GINNY
Right now you're over a year old, am I right?

HARRY
A year and three months.

GINNY
That's a year and three months she could have killed you in. Even now, she's been in Godric's Hollow for twenty-four hours. What's she waiting for?

HARRY
I'm still not entirely following—

GINNY
What if she's not waiting for you – she's waiting for him . . . to stop him?

HARRY

What?

GINNY

Delphi's picked tonight because he's here – because her father is coming. She wants to meet him. Be with him, the father she loves. Voldemort's problems started when he attacked you. If he hadn't done that . . .

HARRY

He'd have only got more powerful – the darkness would only have got darker.

GINNY

The best way to break the prophecy is not to kill Harry Potter, it's to stop Voldemort doing anything at all.

ACT FOUR SCENE TEN

GODRIC'S HOLLOW, CHURCH, 1981

The group are gathered and full of confusion.

RON
> So let me get this right – we're fighting to protect
> Voldemort?

ALBUS
> Voldemort killing my grandparents. Voldemort trying to
> kill my dad?

HERMIONE
> Of course, Ginny. Delphi's not trying to kill Harry – she's
> stopping Voldemort trying to kill Harry. Brilliant.

DRACO
> So – we just wait? Until Voldemort turns up?

ALBUS
> Does she know when he does turn up? Hasn't she come here
> twenty-four hours early because she isn't sure when he'll
> arrive and in what direction? The history books – correct
> me if I'm wrong, Scorpius – show nothing about when and
> how he arrived in Godric's Hollow?

SCORPIUS *and* HERMIONE
> You're not wrong.

RON

Blimey! There are two of them!

DRACO

So how can we use this to our advantage?

ALBUS

Do you know what I'm really good at?

HARRY

There's plenty you're good at, Albus.

ALBUS

Polyjuicing. And I think Bathilda Bagshot may have all the ingredients for Polyjuice in her basement. We can Polyjuice into Voldemort and bring her to us.

RON

To use Polyjuice you need a bit of someone. We don't have a bit of Voldemort.

HERMIONE

But I like the concept, a pretend mouse for her cat.

HARRY

How close can we get through transfiguration?

HERMIONE

We know what he looks like. We've got some excellent wizards and witches here.

GINNY

You want to transfigure into Voldemort?

ALBUS

It's the only way.

HERMIONE

It is, isn't it?

RON *steps forward bravely.*

RON

Then I would like to – I think I should be him. I mean, it won't be – exactly nice being Voldemort – but without wishing to blow my own trumpet – I am probably the most chilled out of all of us and . . . so maybe transfiguring into

him – into the Dark Lord will do less damage to me than –
any of you more – intense – people.

HARRY *steps away, introspective.*

HERMIONE
Who are you calling intense?

DRACO
I'd also like to volunteer. I think being Voldemort requires
precision ... no offence, Ron ... and a knowledge of Dark
Magic, and—

HERMIONE
And I'd like to volunteer, too. As Minister for Magic I think
it's my responsibility and right.

SCORPIUS
Maybe we should draw lots—

DRACO
You're not volunteering, Scorpius.

ALBUS
Actually—

GINNY
No, no way. I think you're all mad. I know what that voice
is like inside your head. I won't have it in mine again—

HARRY
And anyway – it has to be me.

Everyone turns to HARRY.

DRACO
What?

HARRY
For this plan to work she has to believe it's him, without
hesitation. She'll use Parseltongue – and I *knew* there was
a reason why I still have that ability. But more than that,
I – know what it is to feel – like him. I know what it is to *be*
him. It has to be me.

RON

Rubbish. Beautifully put, but beautiful rubbish. No way are you going to—

HERMIONE

I'm afraid you're right, my old friend.

RON

Hermione, you're wrong, Voldemort is not something to be – Harry should not—

GINNY

And I hate to agree with my brother, but . . .

RON

He could get stuck – as Voldemort – forever.

HERMIONE

Your concerns are valid but . . .

HARRY

Hang on, Hermione. Gin.

GINNY *and* HARRY *make eye contact.*

I won't do it if you don't want me to. But it feels like the only way to me. Am I wrong?

GINNY *thinks a moment and then softly nods.* HARRY's *face hardens.*

GINNY

You're right.

HARRY

Then let's do this.

DRACO

Don't we need to discuss the route you're taking – the—

HARRY

She's watching for him. She'll come to me.

DRACO

And then what? When she's with you? May I remind you this is a very powerful witch.

RON
> Easy. He gets her in here. We zap her together.

DRACO
> 'Zap her'?

> HERMIONE *looks around the room.*

HERMIONE
> We'll hide behind these doors. If you can get her to this
> point Harry (*she indicates the point where the light from the
> church's Rose Window hits the floor*), then we come out and
> make sure she has no chance to escape.

RON (*with a look to* DRACO)
> And then we'll *zap* her.

HERMIONE
> Harry, last chance, are you sure you can do this?

HARRY
> Yes, I can do this.

DRACO
> No, there's too many what ifs – too many things that can
> go wrong – the transfiguration could not hold, she could
> see through it – if she escapes us now there's no telling the
> damage she can do – we need time to properly plan to—

ALBUS
> Draco, trust my dad. He won't let us down.

> HARRY *looks at* ALBUS *– moved.*

HERMIONE
> Wands.

> *Everyone withdraws their wands.* HARRY *clasps his.*
> *There's a light that builds – that overwhelms.*
> *The transfiguration is slow and monstrous.*
> *And the form of* VOLDEMORT *emerges from* HARRY*. And
> it's horrendous. He turns. He looks around his friends
> and family. They look back – aghast.*

RON
    Bloody hell.

HARRY/VOLDEMORT
    It worked, then?

GINNY (*gravely*)
    Yes. It worked.

ACT FOUR   SCENE ELEVEN

GODRIC'S HOLLOW, CHURCH, 1981

RON, HERMIONE, DRACO, SCORPIUS *and* ALBUS *stand at the window, looking out.* GINNY *can't look. She sits further back.*

ALBUS notices his mum sitting apart. He walks over to her.

ALBUS
It's going to be okay, you know that, Mum?

GINNY
I know it is. Or I hope I do. I just – don't want to see him like that. The man I love shrouded in the man I hate.

ALBUS sits beside his mum.

ALBUS
I liked her, Mum. You know that? I really liked her. Delphi. And she was – Voldemort's daughter?

GINNY
That's what they're good at Albus – catching innocents in their web.

ALBUS
This is all my fault.

GINNY takes ALBUS in her arms.

GINNY
How funny. Your dad seems to think it's all his. Strange pair, you are.

SCORPIUS *hisses from the door, interrupting her.*

SCORPIUS
That's her. That's her. She's seen him.

HERMIONE
Positions. Everybody. And remember, don't come out until he's got her in the light. We've one shot at this, we don't want to mess it up.

They all move fast.

DRACO
Hermione Granger, I'm being bossed around by Hermione Granger. (*She turns towards him, he smiles.*) And I'm mildly enjoying it.

SCORPIUS
Dad ...

They scatter. They hide behind two major doors.
HARRY/VOLDEMORT *re-enters the church. He walks a few paces and then he turns.*

HARRY/VOLDEMORT
Whichever witch or wizard is following me, I assure you, you will regret it.

DELPHI *emerges behind him. She is compelled to him. This is her father and this is the moment she's waited for her entire life.*

DELPHI
Lord Voldemort. It is me. I am following you.

HARRY/VOLDEMORT
I do not know you. Leave me.

She breathes deeply.

DELPHI
I am your daughter.

HARRY/VOLDEMORT
If you were my daughter, I'd know of you.

DELPHI *looks at him imploringly.*

DELPHI
I am from the future. The child of Bellatrix Lestrange
and you. I was born in Malfoy Manor before the Battle of
Hogwarts. A battle you are going to lose. I have come to
save you.

HARRY/VOLDEMORT *turns. She meets his eyes.*

It was Rodolphus Lestrange, Bellatrix's loyal husband, who
on return from Azkaban told me who I was and revealed
the prophecy he thought I was destined to fulfil. I am your
daughter, sir.

HARRY/VOLDEMORT
I am familiar with Bellatrix and there are certain
similarities in your face – though you haven't inherited the
best of her. But without proof . . .

DELPHI *speaks intently in Parseltongue.*
HARRY/VOLDEMORT *laughs viciously.*

That's your proof?

DELPHI *effortlessly rises into the air.* HARRY/VOLDEMORT
steps back – amazed.

DELPHI
I am the Augurey to your Dark Lord, and I am ready to give
all that I have to serve you.

HARRY/VOLDEMORT *(trying not to show his shock)*
You learnt flight – from – me?

DELPHI
I have tried to follow the path you set.

HARRY/VOLDEMORT
I have never met a witch or a wizard who's attempted to be
my equal before.

DELPHI
Do not mistake me – I would not claim to be worthy of you,

Lord. But I have devoted my life to being a child you could
be proud of.

HARRY/VOLDEMORT *(interrupting)*
I see what you are, and I see what you could be. Daughter.

She looks at him, desperately moved.

DELPHI
Father?

HARRY/VOLDEMORT
Together, the power we could wield.

DELPHI
Father . . .

HARRY/VOLDEMORT
Come here, in the light, so I may examine what my blood
made.

DELPHI
Your mission is a mistake. Attacking Harry Potter is a
mistake. He will destroy you.

*HARRY/VOLDEMORT's hand turns into HARRY's hand. He
looks at it astonished and dismayed, and then quickly
pulls it inside his sleeve.*

HARRY/VOLDEMORT
He is a baby.

DELPHI
He has his mother's love, your spell will rebound, destroying
you and making him too powerful and you too weak. You
will recover, to spend the next seventeen years consumed in
a battle with him – a battle you will lose.

*HARRY/VOLDEMORT's hair begins to sprout, he feels it, he
attempts to cover it. He pulls his hood over his head.*

HARRY/VOLDEMORT
Then I won't attack him. You are right.

DELPHI
Father?

HARRY/VOLDEMORT *shrinks down – he is now more* HARRY *than* VOLDEMORT. *He turns his back to* DELPHI.

Father?

HARRY *(trying desperately to still sound like* VOLDEMORT*)*
Your plan is a good one. The fight is off. You have served me well, now come here into the light so I may examine you.

> DELPHI *sees a door slightly sway open and then be pulled shut. She frowns at it, thinking rapidly, her suspicion growing.*

DELPHI
Father . . .

> *She tries to get a glimpse of his face again, there is almost a dance happening here.*

You are not Lord Voldemort.

> DELPHI *unleashes a bolt from her hand.* HARRY *matches her.*

Incendio!

HARRY
Incendio!

> *The bolts meet in a beautiful explosion in the middle of the room.*
> *And with her other hand* DELPHI *sends bolts to both doors as the others try to open them.*

DELPHI
Potter. Colloportus!

> HARRY *looks at the doors, dismayed.*

GINNY *(from off)*
She's sealed the doors from your side.

DELPHI
What? Thought your friends were going to join you did you?

HERMIONE (*from off*)
Harry ... Harry ...

HARRY
Fine. I'll deal with you alone.

He moves to attack her again. But she is far stronger.
HARRY's wand ascends towards her. He is disarmed. He is
helpless.

How did you ... ? What are you?

DELPHI
I've watched you for a long time, Harry Potter. I know you
better than my father did.

HARRY
You think you've learnt my weaknesses?

DELPHI
I've studied to be worthy of him! Yes, even though he is the
supreme wizard of all time, he will be proud of me. Expulso!

HARRY rolls away as the floor explodes behind him. He
crawls frantically under a church pew, trying to work out
how he can fight her.

Are you crawling away from me? Harry Potter. Hero of the
wizarding world. Crawling away like a rat. Wingardium
Leviosa!

The church pew ascends into the air.

The question is whether it's worth my time to kill you,
knowing that as soon as I stop my father, your destruction
will be assured. How to decide? Oh, I'm bored, I'll kill you.

She sends down the pew hard down upon him. It smashes
as he rolls desperately away.

ALBUS emerges from a grate on the floor, neither notice.

Avada—

ALBUS
   Dad ...

HARRY
   Albus! No!

> *ALBUS throws HARRY one of the wands. HARRY catches it,*
> *full of consternation about the risk his son his taken.*

DELPHI
   Two of you? Choices, choices. I think I'll kill the boy first.
   Avada Kedavra!

> *She fires the Killing Curse at ALBUS — but HARRY throws*
> *him out of the way. The bolt smashes into the ground.*
> *He fires a bolt back.*

You think you're stronger than me?

HARRY
   No. I'm not.

> *They fire bolts mercilessly at each other as ALBUS rolls*
> *quickly away and slams a spell into one door and then*
> *another, opening them.*

ALBUS
   Alohomora!

HARRY
   But we are.

ALBUS
   Alohomora!

HARRY
   I've never fought alone, you see. And I never will.

> *HERMIONE, RON, GINNY and DRACO emerge from the*
> *doors, and fire up their spells at DELPHI, who screams out*
> *in exasperation. This is titanic. But she can't fight them*
> *all.*
> *There are a series of bangs — and then, overpowered and*
> *devastated, DELPHI tumbles down to the floor.*

DELPHI
No ... No ...

HERMIONE
Brachiabindo!

She's bound.

HARRY advances towards DELPHI. He doesn't take his eyes off her. All the others stay back.

HARRY
Albus, are you okay?

ALBUS
Yes, Dad, I'm okay.

HARRY still doesn't take his eyes off DELPHI. He's still scared of her.

HARRY
Ginny, has he been injured? I need to know he's safe ...

GINNY
He insisted. He was the only one small enough to crawl through the grate. I tried to stop him.

HARRY
Just tell me he's okay.

ALBUS
I'm fine, Dad. I promise.

HARRY keeps advancing towards DELPHI.

HARRY
A lot of people have tried to hurt me – but my son! You dare hurt my son!

DELPHI
I only wanted to know my father.

These words take HARRY by surprise.

HARRY
You can't remake your life. You'll always be an orphan. That never leaves you.

DELPHI
Just let me – see him.

HARRY
I can't and I won't.

DELPHI (*truly pitiful*)
Then kill me.

HARRY *thinks a moment.*

HARRY
I can't do that either . . .

ALBUS
What? Dad? She's dangerous.

HARRY
No, Albus . . .

ALBUS
But she's a murderer – I've seen her murder—

HARRY *turns and looks at his son and then at* GINNY.

HARRY
Yes. Albus, she's a murderer, and we're not.

HERMIONE
We have to be better than them.

RON
Yeah, it's annoying but it's what we learnt.

DELPHI
Take my mind. Take my memory. Make me forget who I am.

RON
No. We'll take you back to our time.

HERMIONE
And you'll go to Azkaban. Same as your mother.

DRACO
Where you'll rot.

HARRY *hears a noise. A hissing noise.*

*And then there is a noise like death – a noise like nothing
else we've heard before.*

Haaarry Pottttter . . .

SCORPIUS
What's that?

HARRY
No. No. Not yet.

ALBUS
What?

RON
Voldemort.

DELPHI
Father?

HERMIONE
Now? Here?

DELPHI
Father!

DRACO
Silencio! (DELPHI *is gagged.*) Wingardium Leviosa! (*She is sent
upwards and away.*)

HARRY
He's coming. He's coming right now.

> VOLDEMORT *comes through the back of stage, and across
> it, and walks down into the auditorium. And the air fills
> with the hatred and fear he spreads. He brings death with
> him. And everyone knows it.*

ACT FOUR   SCENE TWELVE

GODRIC'S HOLLOW, 1981

HARRY *looks after* VOLDEMORT *helplessly.*

HARRY
Voldemort is going to kill my mum and dad, and there's nothing I can do to stop him.

DRACO
That's not true.

SCORPIUS
Dad, now is not the time . . .

ALBUS
There is something you could do – to stop him. But you won't.

DRACO
That's heroic.

GINNY *takes* HARRY's *hand.*

GINNY
You don't have to watch, Harry. We can go home.

HARRY
I'm letting it happen . . . of course I have to watch.

HERMIONE
Then we'll all witness it.

RON

We'll all watch.

We hear unfamiliar voices . . .

JAMES (*from off*)

Lily, take Harry and go! It's him! Go! Run! I'll hold him off . . .

There is a blast, and then a laugh.

You keep away, you understand – you keep away.

VOLDEMORT (*from off*)

Avada Kedavra!

> HARRY *flinches as green light flashes around the auditorium.*
>
> ALBUS *takes his hand.* HARRY *grasps hold of it. He needs it.*

ALBUS

He did everything he could.

> GINNY *rises beside* HARRY, *and takes his other hand. He leans into them, they're holding him up now.*

HARRY

That's my mum, at the window. I can see my mother, she looks beautiful.

There's the sound of banging as doors are blasted off.

LILY (*from off*)

Not Harry, not Harry, please not Harry . . .

VOLDEMORT (*from off*)

Stand aside, you silly girl . . . stand aside now . . .

LILY (*from off*)

Not Harry, please no, take me, kill me instead . . .

VOLDEMORT (*from off*)

This is my last warning—

ACT FOUR   SCENE TWELVE

LILY (*from off*)
>Not Harry! Please ... have mercy ... have mercy ... not my
>son! Please – I'll do anything.

VOLDEMORT (*from off*)
>Avada Kedavra!

>*And it's like lightning passes through* HARRY's *body. He's
>sent to the floor, a pure mess of grief.*
>*And a noise like a shrunken scream descends and ascends
>around us.*
>*And we just watch.*
>*And slowly what was there is no longer there.*
>*And the stage transforms and rotates.*
>*And* HARRY *and his family and his friends are rotated off
>and away.*

ACT FOUR SCENE THIRTEEN

GODRIC'S HOLLOW, INSIDE JAMES AND
LILY POTTER'S HOUSE, 1981

And we're in the burning ruins of a broken house. A house that has undergone a vicious attack.

HAGRID emerges into it and walks through the ruins.

HAGRID
James?

He looks about himself.

Lily??

He walks slowly, unwilling to see too much too soon. He is entirely overwhelmed.
And then he sees them, and he stops, and he says nothing.
And we watch as the pain grows across his face.

Oh. Oh. That's not – that's not – I weren't ... they told me, but – I were hoping for better ...

He looks at them, as if unwilling to believe it's true, and then bows his head. He mutters a few words and then takes some crumpled flowers from his deep pockets and lays them on the floor.

I'm sorry, they told me, he told me, Dumbledore told me, I can't wait with yeh. Them Muggles are coming yeh see with their flashing blues and they won't 'preciate a big lummox like me would they?

He lets out a sob.

Hard though it is to leave yeh. I want yeh to know – yeh won't be forgotten – not by me – not by anyfolk.

And then he hears a sound – the sound of a baby snuffling. HAGRID *turns towards it, walking with more intensity now.*

He looks down and stands over the crib, which seems to radiate light.

Well. Hello. Yeh must be Harry. Hello, Harry Potter. I'm Rubeus Hagrid. And I'm gonna be yer friend whether yeh like it or not. 'Cos yeh've had it tough, not that yeh know it yet. An' yer gonna need friends. Now yeh best come with me don't yeh think?

As flashing blue lights fill the room giving it an almost ethereal glow, he lifts HARRY *gently into his arms.*

And then – without looking back – he strides away through the house.

And we descend into soft black.

ACT FOUR   SCENE FOURTEEN

HOGWARTS, CLASSROOM

SCORPIUS *and* ALBUS *run into a room, full of excitement. They slam the door after themselves.*

SCORPIUS
I can't quite believe I did that.

ALBUS
I can't quite believe you did that either.

SCORPIUS
Rose Granger-Weasley. I asked out Rose Granger-Weasley.

ALBUS
And she said no.

SCORPIUS
But I asked her. I planted the acorn. The acorn that will grow into our eventual marriage.

ALBUS
You are aware that you're an utter fantasist.

SCORPIUS
And I'd agree with you – only Polly Chapman did ask me to the School Ball . . .

ALBUS
In an alternate reality where you were significantly – really significantly, more popular – a different girl asked you out – and that means—

SCORPIUS

And yes, logic would dictate I should be pursuing Polly – or allowing her to pursue me – she's a notorious beauty after all – but a Rose is a Rose.

ALBUS

You know logic would dictate that you're a freak? Rose hates you.

SCORPIUS

Correction, she used to hate me, but did you see the look in her eyes when I asked? That wasn't hate, that was pity.

ALBUS

And pity's good?

SCORPIUS

Pity is a start my friend, a foundation on which to build a palace – a palace of lurve.

ALBUS

I honestly thought I'd be the first of us to get a girlfriend.

SCORPIUS

Oh, you will, undoubtedly, probably that new smoky-eyed Potions professor – she's old enough for you, right?

ALBUS

I don't have a thing about older women!

SCORPIUS

And you've got time – a lot of time – to seduce her. Because Rose is going to take years to persuade.

ALBUS

I admire your confidence.

ROSE comes past them on the stairs, she looks at them both.

ROSE

Hi.

Neither boy knows quite how to reply – she looks at SCORPIUS.

ROSE

This is only going to be weird if you let it be weird.

SCORPIUS

Received and entirely understood.

ROSE

Okay. 'Scorpion King'.

She walks off with a smile on her face. SCORPIUS *and*
ALBUS *look at each other.* ALBUS *grins and punches*
SCORPIUS *on the arm.*

ALBUS

Maybe you're right – pity is a start.

SCORPIUS

Are you heading to Quidditch? Slytherin are playing
Hufflepuff – it's a big one—

ALBUS

I thought we hated Quidditch?

SCORPIUS

People can change. Besides, I've been practising. I think I
might make the team this year. Come on.

ALBUS

I can't. My dad's arranged to come up—

SCORPIUS

He's taking time away from the Ministry?

ALBUS

He wants to go on a walk – something to show me – share
with me – something.

SCORPIUS

A walk?

ALBUS

I know, I think it's a bonding thing or something similarly
vomit-inducing. Still, you know, I think I'll go.

SCORPIUS *reaches in and hugs* ALBUS.

What's this? I thought we decided we don't hug.

SCORPIUS

I wasn't sure. Whether we should. In this new version of us I had in my head.

ALBUS

Better ask Rose if it's the right thing to do.

SCORPIUS

Ha! Yeah. Right.

The two boys dislocate and grin at each other.

ALBUS

I'll see you at dinner.

ACT FOUR SCENE FIFTEEN

A BEAUTIFUL HILL

HARRY *and* ALBUS *walk up a hill on a beautiful summer's day.*
They say nothing, enjoying the sun on their faces as they climb.

HARRY
So are you ready?

ALBUS
For what?

HARRY
Well, there's the fourth-year exams – and then the fifth
year – big year – in my fifth year I did—

He looks at ALBUS. *He smiles. He talks quickly.*

I did a lot of stuff. Some of it good. Some of it bad. A lot of
it quite confusing.

ALBUS
Good to know.

HARRY smiles.

I got to watch them – you know – for a bit – your mum and
dad. They were – you had fun together. Your dad used to
love to do this smoke ring thing with you where you . . .
well, you couldn't stop giggling.

HARRY
Yes?

ALBUS
I think you'd have liked them. And I think I would have
liked them too.

*HARRY nods. There's a faintly uncomfortable silence. Both
are trying to reach each other here, both are failing.*

HARRY
You know, I thought I'd lost him – Voldemort – I thought
I'd lost him – and then my scar started hurting again and
I had dreams of him and I could even speak Parseltongue
again and I started to feel like I'd not changed at all – that
he'd never let me go –

ALBUS
And had he?

HARRY
The part of me that was Voldemort died a long time ago,
but it wasn't enough to be physically rid of him – I had to
be mentally rid of him. And that – is a lot to learn for a
forty-year-old man.

He looks at ALBUS.

That thing I said to you – it was unforgiveable, and I can't
ask you to forget it but I can hope we move past it.

I'm going to try to be a better dad for you, Albus. I am going
to try and – be honest with you and . . .

ALBUS
Dad, you don't need to—

HARRY
You told me you don't think I'm scared of anything, and
that – I mean, I'm scared of everything. I mean, I'm afraid
of the dark, did you know that?

ALBUS
Harry Potter is afraid of the dark?

HARRY

I don't like small spaces and – I've never told anyone this but I don't much like – (*he hesitates before saying this*) pigeons.

ALBUS

You don't like pigeons?

HARRY (*he scrunches up his face*)

Nasty, pecky, dirty things. They give me the creeps.

ALBUS

But pigeons are harmless!

HARRY

I know. But the thing that scares me most, Albus Severus Potter, is being a dad to you. Because I'm operating without wires here. Most people at least have a dad to base themselves on – and either try to be or try not to be. I've got nothing – or very little. So I'm learning, okay? And I'm going to try with everything I've got – to be a good dad for you.

ALBUS

And I'll try and be a better son. I know I'm not James, Dad, I'll never be like you two—

HARRY

James is nothing like me.

ALBUS

Isn't he?

HARRY

Everything comes easy for James. My childhood was a constant struggle.

ALBUS

So was mine. So you're saying – am I – like you?

HARRY *smiles at* ALBUS.

HARRY

Actually you're more like your mum – bold, fierce, funny – which I like – which I think makes you a pretty great son.

ALBUS

I almost destroyed the world.

HARRY

Delphi wasn't going anywhere, Albus – you brought her out into the light and you found a way for us to fight her. You may not see it now, but you saved us.

ALBUS

But shouldn't I have done better?

HARRY

You don't think I ask myself the same questions?

ALBUS (*stomach sinking further, he knows this is not what his dad would do*)

And then – when we caught her – I wanted to kill her.

HARRY

You'd watched her murder Craig, you were angry Albus, and that's okay. And you wouldn't have done it.

ALBUS

How do you know that? Maybe that's my Slytherin side. Maybe that's what the Sorting Hat saw in me.

HARRY

I don't understand your head, Albus – actually, you know what, you're a teenager, I shouldn't be able to understand your head, but I do understand your heart. I didn't – for a long time – but thanks to this – 'escapade' – I know what you got in there. Slytherin, Gryffindor, whatever label you've been given – I know – know – that heart is a good one – yeah, whether you like it or not, you're on your way to being some wizard.

ALBUS

Oh, I'm not going to be a wizard, I'm going into pigeon racing. I'm quite excited about it.

HARRY *grins.*

HARRY

Those names you have – they shouldn't be a burden. Albus
Dumbledore had his trials too you know – and Severus
Snape, well, you know all about him—

ALBUS

They were good men.

HARRY

They were great men, with huge flaws, and you know
what – those flaws almost made them greater.

ALBUS *looks around himself.*

ALBUS

Dad? Why are we here?

HARRY

This is where I often come.

ALBUS

But this is a graveyard ...

HARRY

And here is Cedric's grave ...

ALBUS

Dad?

HARRY

The boy who was killed – Craig Bowker – how well did you
know him?

ALBUS

Not well enough.

HARRY

I didn't know Cedric well enough either. He could have
played Quidditch for England. Or been a brilliant Auror.
He could have been anything. And Amos is right – he was
stolen. So I come here. Just to say sorry. When I can.

ALBUS

That's a – good thing to do.

ALBUS *joins his dad in front of* CEDRIC's *grave.* HARRY
smiles at his son and looks up at the sky.

HARRY
I think it's going to be a nice day.

He touches his son's shoulder. And the two of them – just slightly – melt together.

ALBUS *(smiles)*
So do I.

THE END

Harry Potter and the Cursed Child Parts One and Two was first produced by Sonia Friedman Productions, Colin Callender and Harry Potter Theatrical Productions. It premiered at the Palace Theatre, London, on 30 July 2016.

Original London cast in alphabetical order

CRAIG BOWKER JR	Jeremy Ang Jones
MOANING MYRTLE, LILY POTTER SR	Annabel Baldwin
UNCLE VERNON, SEVERUS SNAPE, LORD VOLDEMORT	Paul Bentall
SCORPIUS MALFOY	Anthony Boyle
ALBUS POTTER	Sam Clemmett
HERMIONE GRANGER	Noma Dumezweni
POLLY CHAPMAN	Claudia Grant
HAGRID, SORTING HAT	Chris Jarman
YANN FREDERICKS	James Le Lacheur
AUNT PETUNIA, MADAM HOOCH, DOLORES UMBRIDGE	Helena Lymbery
AMOS DIGGORY, ALBUS DUMBLEDORE	Barry McCarthy
TROLLEY WITCH, PROFESSOR McGONAGALL	Sandy McDade
STATION MASTER	Adam McNamara
GINNY POTTER	Poppy Miller
CEDRIC DIGGORY, JAMES POTTER JR, JAMES POTTER SR	Tom Milligan

DUDLEY DURSLEY, KARL JENKINS, VIKTOR KRUM	Jack North
HARRY POTTER	Jamie Parker
DRACO MALFOY	Alex Price
BANE	Nuno Silva
ROSE GRANGER-WEASLEY, YOUNG HERMIONE	Cherrelle Skeete
DELPHI DIGGORY	Esther Smith
RON WEASLEY	Paul Thornley

YOUNG HARRY POTTER
{
Rudi Goodman
Alfred Jones
Bili Keogh
Ewan Rutherford
Nathaniel Smith
Dylan Standen
}

LILY POTTER JR
{
Zoe Brough
Cristina Fray
Christiana Hutchings
}

OTHER ROLES PLAYED BY

Nicola Alexis, Jeremy Ang Jones, Rosemary Annabella,
Annabel Baldwin, Jack Bennett, Paul Bentall, Claudia Grant,
James Howard, Lowri James, Chris Jarman, Martin Johnston,
James Le Lacheur, Helena Lymbery, Barry McCarthy,
Andrew McDonald, Adam McNamara, Tom Milligan,
Jack North, Stuart Ramsay, Nuno Silva, Cherrelle Skeete

SWINGS

Helen Aluko, Matthew Bancroft, Morag Cross, Chipo Kureya,
Tom Mackley, Joshua Wyatt

Nuno Silva	Resident Movement Director
Jack North	Assistant Movement Captain
Morag Cross	Voice Captain

CREATIVE AND
PRODUCTION TEAM 2017

Original Story	J.K. Rowling, John Tiffany, Jack Thorne
Playwright	Jack Thorne
Director	John Tiffany
Movement Director	Steven Hoggett
Set Designer	Christine Jones
Costume Designer	Katrina Lindsay
Composer & Arranger	Imogen Heap
Lighting Designer	Neil Austin
Sound Designer	Gareth Fry
Illusions & Magic	Jamie Harrison
Music Supervisor & Arranger	Martin Lowe
Casting Director	Julia Horan CDG
Production Manager	Gary Beestone
Production Stage Manager	Sam Hunter
Associate Director	Des Kennedy
Associate Movement Director	Neil Bettles
Associate Set Designer	Brett J. Banakis

Associate Sound Designer	Pete Malkin
Illusions & Magic Associate	Chris Fisher
Casting Associate	Lotte Hines
Assistant Lighting Designer	Adam King
Costume Design Supervisor	Sabine Lemaître
Hair, Wigs & Make-up	Carole Hancock
Props Supervisors	Lisa Buckley, Mary Halliday
Music Editor	Phij Adams
Music Production	Imogen Heap
Special Effects	Jeremy Chernick
Video Design	Finn Ross, Ash Woodward
Dialect Coach	Daniele Lydon
Voice Coach	Richard Ryder
Resident Director	Pip Minnithorpe
Company Stage Manager	Richard Clayton
Stage Manager	Jordan Noble-Davies
Deputy Stage Manager	Jenefer Tait
Assistant Stage Managers	Oliver Bagwell Purefoy, Tom Gilding, Sally Inch, Ben Sherratt
Head of Wardrobe	Amy Gillot
Deputy Head of Wardrobe	Laura Watkins
Wardrobe Assistants	Kate Anderson, Leanne Hired
Dressers	George Amielle, Melissa Cooke, Rosie Etheridge, John Ovenden, Emilee Swift
Daytime Wardrobe Assistant	Melissa Hadley
Head of Hair, Wigs & Make-up	Nina Van Houten
Deputy Head of Hair, Wigs & Make-up	Alice Townes

Hair, Wigs & Make-up Assistants	Jacob Fessey, Cassie Murphie, Joanna Sim
Head of Sound	Chris Reid
Deputy Head of Sound	Rowena Edwards
Sound No. 3	Laura Head
Sound No. 4	Bethany Woodford
SFX Operator	Callum Donaldson
Head of Automation	Josh Peters
Deputy Head of Automation	Jamie Lawrence
Automation No. 3	Jamie Robson
Show Chief LX	David Treanor
Deputy Show Chief LX	Paddy Magee
Performer Flying Technician	Paul Gurney
Chaperones	David Russell, Eleanor Dowling

General Management	Sonia Friedman Productions
Executive Director	Diane Benjamin
Executive Producer	Pam Skinner
Associate Producers	Fiona Stewart, Ben Canning
Assistant General Manager	Max Bittleston
Production Assistant	Imogen Clare-Wood
Marketing Manager	Meg Massey
Head of Sales and Revenue	Mark Payn
Associate Producer (Development)	Lucie Lovatt
Literary Associate	Jack Bradley
House Seats Assistant	Tobias Jones

BIOGRAPHIES OF THE ORIGINAL STORY TEAM

J.K. ROWLING
Original story

J.K. Rowling is the author of the seven Harry Potter novels, which have sold over 450 million copies and have been translated into 79 languages, and three companion books originally published for charity. She has also written *The Casual Vacancy*, a novel for adults, and, under the pseudonym of Robert Galbraith, is the author of the Cormoran Strike crime series. In 2016 J.K. Rowling made her screenwriting debut and was a producer on the film *Fantastic Beasts and Where to Find Them*, a further extension of the Wizarding World, and the start of a new five-film series.

JOHN TIFFANY
Original story and director

John Tiffany directed *Once*, for which he was the recipient of multiple awards on Broadway, in the West End and internationally. Other recent credits include *The Glass Menagerie* at A.R.T., on Broadway, EIF and the West End and *The Ambassador* at BAM. As Associate Director of the Royal Court, his work includes *The Twits*, *Hope* and *The Pass*. He was the director of *Let the Right One In* for the National Theatre of Scotland, which transferred to the Royal Court, West End and St Ann's Warehouse, and toured internationally. His other work for the National Theatre of Scotland includes *Macbeth* (also Lincoln Center and Broadway), *Enquirer*, *The Missing*, *Peter Pan*, *The House of Bernarda Alba*, *Transform Caithness: Hunter*, *Be Near Me*, *Nobody Will Ever Forgive Us*, *The Bacchae* (also Lincoln Center), *Elizabeth Gordon Quinn*, *Home: Glasgow* and *Black Watch*, which toured internationally and for which he won Olivier and Critics' Circle Awards. He was Associate Director of the Traverse Theatre from 1996 to 2001, Paines Plough from 2001 to 2005, the National Theatre of Scotland from 2005 to 2012 and was a Radcliffe Fellow at Harvard University in the 2010–2011 academic year.

JACK THORNE
Original story and playwright

Jack Thorne writes for theatre, film, television and radio. His theatre credits include *Hope* and *Let the Right One In*, both directed by John Tiffany, *Junkyard*, a Headlong, Rose Theatre Kingston, Bristol Old Vic & Theatr Clwyd co-production, *The Solid Life of Sugar Water* for the Graeae Theatre Company and the National Theatre, *Bunny* for the Edinburgh Fringe Festival, *Stacy* for the Trafalgar Studios, and *2nd May 1997* and *When You Cure Me* for the Bush. His adaptations include *The Physicists* for the Donmar Warehouse and *Stuart: A Life Backwards* for HighTide. On film his credits include *War Book*, *A Long Way Down* and *The Scouting Book for Boys*. For television his credits include *The Last Panthers*, *Don't Take My Baby*, *This Is England*, *The Fades*, *Glue*, *Cast-Offs* and *National Treasure*. He won BAFTAs in 2016 for Best Mini-Series (*This Is England '90*) and Best Single Drama (*Don't Take My Baby*), and in 2012 for Best Drama Series (*The Fades*) and Best Mini-Series (*This Is England '88*).

ACKNOWLEDGEMENTS

All the actors from the Cursed Child workshops, Mel Kenyon, Rachel Taylor, Alexandria Horton, Imogen Clare-Wood, Florence Rees, Jenefer Tait, David Nock, Rachel Mason, Colin, Neil, Sonia, everyone at SFP and The Blair Partnership, Rebecca Salt from JKR PR, Nica Burns and all the staff at the Palace Theatre, and, of course, our incredible cast who helped shape every word.

HARRY POTTER
FAMILY TREE

*An ancient wizarding line, the Potters stretch as far
back as the twelfth century. Since then, the family has
extended into many wizarding and Muggle families:
Peverells, Weasleys, and even Dursleys.*

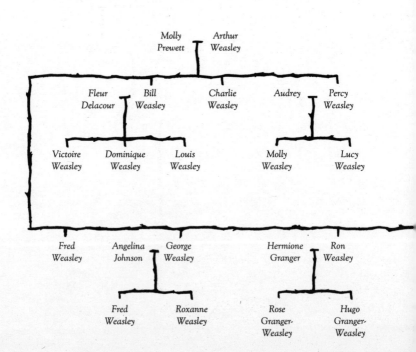

Molly Prewett — Arthur Weasley

Fleur Delacour — Bill Weasley · Charlie Weasley · Audrey — Percy Weasley

Victoire Weasley · Dominique Weasley · Louis Weasley · Molly Weasley · Lucy Weasley

Fred Weasley · Angelina Johnson — George Weasley · Hermione Granger — Ron Weasley

Fred Weasley · Roxanne Weasley · Rose Granger-Weasley · Hugo Granger-Weasley

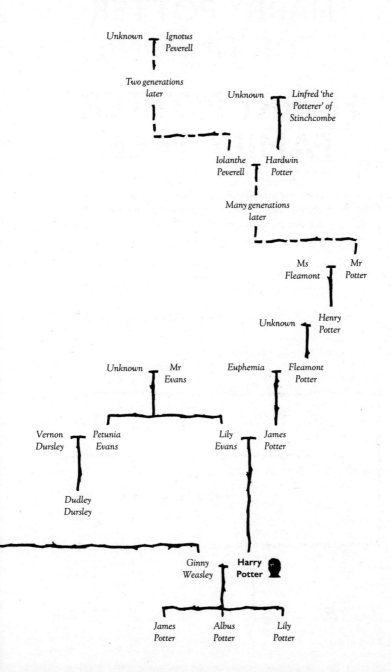

HARRY POTTER:
THE TIMELINE

31 JULY 1980
*Harry Potter is born in
Godric's Hollow, England.*

31 OCTOBER 1981
*Harry's parents, Lily and James Potter,
are murdered in their home by Lord
Voldemort. The now-orphaned Harry
survives Voldemort's killing curse as it
rebounds, leaving a lightning-shaped
scar on his forehead.*

1 NOVEMBER 1981
*Harry is rescued by Hagrid and
brought to live with his Muggle
relatives, the Dursley family, who
deny all knowledge of Harry's roots.*

Ten years later...

PHILOSOPHER'S STONE

31 JULY 1991
*Hagrid gives Harry his
Hogwarts letter and informs
him 'Harry – yer a wizard'.*

1 SEPTEMBER 1991
*On board the Hogwarts Express,
travelling to Hogwarts School
of Witchcraft and Wizardry for
the first time, Harry meets Ron
Weasley and Hermione Granger.*

JUNE 1992
*Harry thwarts Professor
Quirrell's attempt to retrieve the
Philosopher's Stone, and evades
Voldemort for a second time.*

CHAMBER OF SECRETS

31 OCTOBER 1992
*The Chamber of Secrets is opened,
and Slytherin's monster begins
a spate of attacks.*

25 DECEMBER 1992
*Harry, Ron and Hermione take
Polyjuice Potion for the first time.*

MAY 1993
*Harry and Ron enter the Chamber of
Secrets via Moaning Myrtle's bathroom.
Once inside, Harry kills the Basilisk
and destroys Tom Riddle's diary, which
has taken possession of Ginny Weasley.
Harry saves Ginny's life.*

PRISONER OF AZKABAN

AUGUST 1993
In the Daily Prophet, Harry reads of the escaped convict Sirius Black – 'possibly the most infamous prisoner ever to be held in Azkaban fortress'.

1 SEPTEMBER 1993
The Hogwarts Express is intercepted by Dementors.

6 JUNE 1994
Harry realises Sirius is innocent – he has been wrongly accused and Peter Pettigrew is the true culprit.

Harry and Hermione use the Time-Turner to save Sirius, and the guilty Pettigrew escapes for a second time.

GOBLET OF FIRE

AUGUST 1994
The Dark Mark is conjured at the Quidditch World Cup, signifying Voldemort's rise and return to power.

SEPTEMBER–OCTOBER 1994
Professor Dumbledore announces that the Triwizard Tournament will be held for the first time in over a century. Unexpectedly, the Goblet of Fire selects underage Harry to take part, leaving Hogwarts with two champions: Harry Potter and Cedric Diggory.

24 NOVEMBER 1994
In the first Triwizard task, Harry uses his flying skills to retrieve a golden egg from a fire-breathing Hungarian Horntail dragon.

DECEMBER 1994
Viktor Krum, Durmstrang champion, invites Hermione to the Yule Ball. Harry and Ron ask Parvati and Padma Patil.

24 FEBRUARY 1995
In the second Triwizard task, Harry uses Gillyweed to rescue both Ron and Gabrielle Delacour from the Great Lake; the judges are divided over his heroism.

24 JUNE 1995
The final task takes place in a maze full of dangerous creatures and obstacles. Harry and Cedric are joint winners, but the trophy is a Portkey, which transports them to a graveyard where Voldemort and his Death Eaters await. Cedric is murdered and the devastated Harry returns to Hogwarts with Cedric's body – and news of Voldemort's return to power.

ORDER OF THE PHOENIX

SEPTEMBER 1995
Cornelius Fudge, Minister for Magic, refuses to believe Voldemort is back. He appoints Dolores Umbridge, an adversary of Dumbledore, as Defence Against the Dark Arts teacher.

OCTOBER 1995
Harry founds Dumbledore's Army, a group of students who meet in secret to rebel against Umbridge and learn the skills she refuses to teach them.

JUNE 1996
Having fought visions from Voldemort all year, Harry sees Sirius in danger. Accompanied by his closest friends, he goes to the Ministry of Magic and battles Voldemort once more.

MINISTRY OF MAGIC
Harry discovers an important prophecy, which further entwines his fate with Voldemort's.

MINISTRY OF MAGIC
Sirius is murdered by Death Eater Bellatrix Lestrange, and the Ministry's entire stock of Time-Turners is destroyed in the Battle of the Department of Mysteries.

HALF-BLOOD PRINCE

JANUARY 1997
As part of his quest to defeat Voldemort, Dumbledore begins to educate Harry about the Dark Lord's past.

MAY 1997
Harry finally kisses Ginny after Gryffindor wins the Quidditch Cup.

JUNE 1997
Hogwarts is infiltrated by Death Eaters. After Draco Malfoy fails to complete the murderous task set by Voldemort, Severus Snape instead kills Dumbledore.

DEATHLY HALLOWS

AUGUST 1997

The Ministry has fallen and Voldemort has taken power. Harry, Ron and Hermione go on the run, searching for the remaining Horcruxes in the quest to finally defeat the Dark Lord.

DECEMBER 1997

Harry, Ron and Hermione learn of the Deathly Hallows – three objects which, when united, will make the possessor master of Death.

MAY 1998

Harry, Ron and Hermione return to Hogwarts to find the remaining Horcruxes, and the Battle of Hogwarts begins.

BATTLE OF HOGWARTS

Voldemort murders Snape to obtain the Elder Wand in his quest to unite the Deathly Hallows. Harry learns that Snape was in love with his mother Lily; his allegiance was always to Dumbledore and the woman he adored, not to the Dark Lord.

BATTLE OF HOGWARTS

Realising that he is a Horcrux, Harry sacrifices himself to Voldemort to save the Wizarding World.

BATTLE OF HOGWARTS

Neville Longbottom kills Nagini, destroying the final Horcrux in Harry's place.

BATTLE OF HOGWARTS

Harry survives Voldemort's final attack, vanquishing him at last.

Nineteen years later...

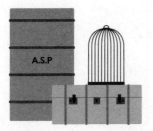

1 SEPTEMBER 2017

Harry (now 37) and Ginny are married with three children. They meet Ron and Hermione Granger-Weasley on platform nine and three-quarters at King's Cross station. Their children, Albus Potter and Rose Granger-Weasley, are starting their first year at Hogwarts. Albus fears he will be placed in Slytherin and Harry assures him: 'Albus Severus, you were named after two headmasters of Hogwarts. One of them was a Slytherin and he was probably the bravest man I ever knew.' The whistle blows and Albus and Rose's journey begins.